Doing Up Small Spaces

Doing Up Small Spaces

Barty Phillips

MEREHURST

Acknowledgements

I would like to thank all those who so kindly lent their homes for photography in this book: Ken Baker; Jon and Sarah Bouchier; Sarah and Nakeeda Cowley; Jane, Phil, Lawrence and George Glynn; Graham Hopewell; Mathew and Chrysta Lipsey; Charlie, Penny and Rosie Phillips Fry; Judith Moore; Jane Priestman; Rachel, Jim and Esme Toler; Oliver and Rhiann Vickars Harris; Toni Willis. And all those others who gave advice and ideas, including Bruce Gornick, Robin and Sue Hodges, and Mick, Pat, Philip, Barbara, Nicky and Kathleen Le Mare.

Acknowledgements are also due for pictures kindly lent to us by Arthur Sanderson and Sons Ltd (page 2); Concord Lighting Ltd (page 55); Crucial Trading Ltd (page 82); Fired Earth (page 87); Onglaze (page 1). Last but not least, I would like to thank the Merehurst team who were patient, meticulous and a pleasure to work with.

Published in 1994 by Merehurst Limited,
Ferry House, 51–57 Lacy Road, Putney, London SW15 1PR

ISBN 1-85391-368-3

A catalogue record of this book is available from the British Library.

Edited by Judy Walker

Designed by Rita Wüthrich

Photography by Jon Bouchier

Typeset by Servis Filmsetting Ltd

Colour separation by Global Colour, Malaysia

Printed in Italy by New Interlitho

Contents

Introduction

In recent years homes have tended to become smaller. The rising cost of housing means that few families can afford to buy large houses, and more people now live on their own. To fill the gap, tiny houses and purpose-built blocks of small flats are being built for first-time buyers and traditional houses are being converted into small apartments.

Of course, people's interests and life-styles should not have to diminish accordingly. In fact, leisure pursuits have increased in the second half of this century and room must be found in the home for sports kit, DIY tools, and music and video equipment. Many people have a computer with all its accessories, and an increasing number of people nowadays work from home.

This makes it doubly important to use all the available space we have. We need to look at our homes with a critical and questioning eye and to make the most of height, odd corners and neglected or half-used areas so that every inch is used to its utmost advantage.

This book suggests imaginative ways of exploiting colour and light, which can create at least the illusion of spaciousness even in cramped areas. It is full of ideas, hints and suggestions which are inexpensive but effective and also points the way to more radical solutions and structural possibilities. Most fundamentally, it shows how to make the best use of all the storage, work, play and display potential in your home.

In many homes, opportunities are missed because tradition gets in the way. To most of us a bedroom is a bedroom, but in a small home this is a self-indulgence. A bedroom can double up as a sewing room, home office or second living room, otherwise it is simply 'dead' space for more than half of the 24 hours. Dual-purpose bedrooms do not need to be unfeminine or unpeaceful or untidy, and the bedroom area can often be separated from the working area by a screen or other room-divider so that the two don't clash.

Equally, the 'glory hole' under the stairs is often unexploited, and yet there are so many uses for this invaluable space which will take the pressure off other parts of the home.

Storage is one of the most important aspects of home-making and, especially in small spaces, needs to be well thought-out to suit each member of the household. The chapter on storage is rich in ideas for all kinds of belongings from jewellery to spare blankets, filing systems and tools. Extra space can often be created in cramped spaces by removing cupboards altogether and finding storage for their contents in other parts of the home.

When it comes to creating the illusion of space, there are many possibilities: mirrors, clever paint effects, imaginative lighting, double-hinged doors which open vistas instead of solid doors to divide rooms.

Using space imaginatively out of necessity is not new, of course. In Wales a farmer's stone cottage in the 19th century consisted of one large room with a fascinating rabbit warren of wooden cubicles piled against the wall at one end, on top of and behind each other, and stepladders leading to each. This compact interlocking of sleeping pockets left the larger space available for all the daytime activities, whereas a bedroom for each person would have taken up the whole cottage. In America the Shakers, a religious sect, designed and built their own plain, unadorned but beautifully crafted furniture. Most designs have a dual purpose or can be hung from the wall when not in use.

I think we have much to learn from the ingenuity of past generations, who knew how to fit their lives into tiny cottages and cramped townhouses. I hope this book will open up ideas and possibilities for today's small-home dwellers.

This kitchen alcove off the living room has one deep red wall, a strong background for the display of equipment and china. All available space under the sloping ceiling has been utilized.

Start with Paint

Colour can be used in many ways to create different effects and to highlight or conceal various aspects of the home. Bold colours in this hallway lead into the blue walls of the room beyond, taking the mind from the narrowness of the space. The colour was softened by dark brown dragged over the orange.

Fresh paint, sympathetic colours and interesting decorative effects will transform the most unpromising raw material. You can create visual illusions, making ceilings appear lower or spaces larger, simply by using paint boldly and with imagination. Modern rooms are often rather box-like but clever use of colour will make all the difference between a claustrophic feeling and a feeling of space and relaxation.

BASIC COLOUR RULES

There are certain accepted principles which can help in choosing paint colours, although once they have been understood there is no compulsion to stick to them. Some very entertaining and pleasing effects can be achieved by breaking away from the rules. However, the basic principles are useful guidelines, especially for beginners.

It is usually best to choose a main colour for the walls and a secondary colour for the ceiling and woodwork (and perhaps for the floor too). White is safe as a main colour, but you may prefer one of the 'nearly white' pale apricot or buff colours available. If you want a more positive colour, you need to know something about the individual characteristics of particular colours.

Bold colours appear to come 'forward' and pale colours tend to recede. Small rooms generally ask for fairly pale colour schemes to make the walls seem farther apart but richer, brighter colours can liven up box-like spaces, particularly kitchens or children's rooms. In these rooms, the paint colours will not be at odds with the furniture, and a feeling of warmth and cosiness may be more important than one of space.

Reds tend to come forward, making a room seem smaller, while blues recede, giving the impression of space. A deep red on all four walls of a small room would probably be too overpowering but one red wall can be cheering, although even then it should be hung with paintings or kitchen equipment so that it acts as a background rather than dominating the room. It could be echoed by splashes of red in the rest of the room to give a unifying effect.

Blues are inclined to make a room feel cool. Rooms which face north or east get little sunlight and always seem chillier than rooms facing south or west, so in the 18th century it was common to paint or paper north-facing rooms in yellows and reds to make them seem warmer; only the south-facing rooms were decorated in blues and greens. If you want a chilly room to feel warmer, choose a warm red, not a bluey red.

Yellow will bring an impression of sunlight into a dark room, but choose an orange-yellow and avoid the greeny tones. Of all colours, yellows can be particularly deceptive; a lovely bright eggyolk colour in the shop may turn a sickly green when you get it home, so choose with care.

Colours can alter depending on the light, the extent of the wall area and the colours they are next to. All colours will appear to change in different circumstances, particularly reds. What seems to be a pale and interesting colour on the colour chart can become oppressive and unpleasant when painted on a large wall, and a colour which appears quite pale on a small area can look much darker over a larger surface. Look at the colour in the natural light from the window as well as under artificial light, and place it next to other colours to see what happens. The eye sees things differently depending on what is next to them. Before going for something really bold, do a test piece first. Be flexible in your thinking and don't expect to get the exact result you want first time. It takes practice and mistakes to become adept, but even if the result is not what you intended you may find you prefer it to your original idea!

USING WHITE

If your home is an interesting shape, full of architectural details such as arches, alcoves, moulded plasterwork and panelling, or if it has a 'cottagey' feel with beams and staircases, you could hardly do better than to paint the walls white.

White will frame the woodwork and provide a neutral background for other colours, as well as for the more interesting architectural elements. White also reflects 75 per cent of light back into the room, so it will help to make dark rooms much lighter. Pale, nearly white colours, although they do have a lightening effect, do not reflect anything like as much light.

White is the colour favoured by most architects for doors, windowframes and sills, skirting boards and so on, and it is hard to go wrong if you do use white for the woodwork. It will set off any other colours you use on the walls and always looks fresh and bright.

Panelled doors or shutters can be slightly emphasized by painting them in three shades of off-white, using the palest colour on the frame, a slightly darker shade on the panels and a marginally darker shade again on the mouldings. The rest of the woodwork should be off-white to co-ordinate the room.

BE ADVENTUROUS WITH COLOUR

It is no good hoping that neutral colours, plain walls and sparse furniture will automatically make a room appear larger or more interesting. It is often better to fill a room with warm colours, strong textures and plenty of books and objects. There are lots of other colours you can use rather than white or pastels and, since paint is the cheapest form of decorating, if you don't like the result you can always paint over it again. So why not be a little adventurous?

No matter what the colour rules may say, your taste is what counts in your own home. Although many people feel quite confident when buying clothes, they are uncertain when it comes to choosing colours and fabrics, largely through lack of practice and experience. Once you start thinking in terms of colour, interesting combinations will begin to jump from magazines, posters,

fabrics, fashion, flowers, leaves, art galleries and even church windows.

Use your camera. Take pictures of colour combinations which intrigue you, buy a small notebook and make notes. Remember that there is no such thing as 'brown' or 'blue'. Brown can be the colour of bread or the colour of mud, the colour of boot polish or a shiny conker. Blue may be sea blue or midnight blue, grey-blue or that wonderful faded greeny blue, bleached by the sun, found on shutters and doors in the Mediterranean. Colours can also be matt or shiny. All have an infinite variety of tones which react differently to different tones

Two bold, contrasting paint colours are used to brighten a dark space and to conceal the under-stair cupboards.

of other colours. It is fascinating to experiment.

Remember too, that what suits an elegant 18th-century room with tall ceilings and generous proportions may not be appropriate for a small, square room with low ceilings. It can be a great help to make a colour board out of a piece of hardboard or stout card, and to pin onto it paint samples and pieces of fabric. Change them about, add to them and take some away until you have a group of colours (and textures) which really pleases you. Keep to one main colour and one secondary colour, or variations of your two colours, perhaps with white as a link.

If you want to create a feeling of space, concentrate on those cool blues and greys which recede into the background. If you prefer to make the room fun to be in and don't care about spaciousness, try a combination of bright, primary colours. Brilliant yellow will give a feeling of warmth, deep blue a feeling of tranquillity, and a balance can be provided with reds and greens in the furniture and fabrics.

In a tiny kitchen, one bright colour can provide a cheerful background for attractive cooking equipment stored on open shelves and hung from hooks, rather than hidden away in cupboards. The kitchen shown on page 7 is a large alcove off a living room and has been created in a piecemeal way, making use of the sloping ceiling to house cupboards which once had another existence in an office. The red wall helps to co-ordinate everything and to give the room an identity of its own, separate to that of the main living room.

SUBTLE PATTERN EFFECTS

Many homes are over-full of shapes, patterns and colours, all shouting for attention. Furniture, wallpaper, books, pictures, fabrics, hi fi, etc. can all add up to a very busy and unrestful feeling.

In small spaces where there is a lot going on, background pattern should be kept very much in the

Designer Graham Hopewell has combined hall, kitchen, dining room, coat cupboard and stairs. Grey 'piping' accentuates the white paint.

background although it need not be eliminated altogether and, indeed, can be useful in covering up poor plasterwork or boring shapes. Textured wallpaper, seemingly made up of pimples, is used far too often to hide blemishes in the walls when the blemishes themselves would be far less hideous than the wallpaper. Instead, to add pattern by painting is cheap, comparatively easy and very satisfying. Decorative and interesting effects can be achieved by various methods, such as sponging, stippling, marbling, antiquing and dragging. These all give character and do not look as 'dead' as flat paint. They will also help to conceal uneven walls.

The yellow walls of this living room have been stencilled with small gold motifs, applied at random over the whole wall.

darker shade in patches over a slightly lighter shade of the same colour.

Generally, these techniques look best in a fairly disciplined household where the finish can be appreciated, otherwise the effect will be wasted and become part of the general chaos.

You will need to experiment with colours and the effect on a test piece of paper may be very different to when colours are seen on the whole wall. Often a quite surprising combination will appeal, such as green and pink or yellow and blue. Some colour combinations only work when both are overlaid with a 'smoky' colour, which tones down what otherwise might be too sugary and links the two colours. Only experimentation can discover the right combination for you. The best way to experiment is on the actual walls, trying a small square of colour and getting used to it for a day or so, then adding a little of another colour or a little white or black until it looks right. You may have the wall completely covered in small squares of different colours before you hit on the one you like. If you choose colours which please you, rather than colours suggested to you as being fashionable, you will find they automatically co-ordinate with your paintings, prints and fabrics.

Simple paint effects give unusual and stylish results without the enormous expense often associated with such sophistication. Decorative paint techniques have a sort of mystique surrounding them but, although the more subtle effects do need great skill, especially when applied to architecturally graceful houses, simple effects can be produced by the relatively inexperienced painter in the sort of homes most of us live in. One or two simple methods are given later in the chapter. Once you have grasped the idea, you can create the soft chalky colours of old Italian plasterwork, the more silky effect of *faux* marbling or the textured impression produced by using a

USING PAINT TO CONCEAL THE WORST

Keeping in mind the characteristics of particular colours, you can manipulate colour to alter the apparent size, breadth, height and mood of a space.

Dark, gloomy rooms
Rooms where daylight is excluded by walls, trees or very small windows are best decorated in pale, bright colours such as yellows, which often manage to produce a lighter, even a sunny, feeling. Mirrors help to double any natural light if they are facing in the right direction, and will also double the amount of colour in the room by reflecting other colours.

Basement rooms, which often receive very little daylight, can be given added warmth by using apricots, reds or oranges. In deep basements where the light has to filter down from street level, it may be better to give up the idea of making the room seem light and instead to create a cosy, cave-like atmosphere. Use deep colours and plenty of low-level lamps with shades which create a glow, rather than direct-beam lights.

Short, squat rooms

Vertical stripes will make a room look taller and narrower. Wide stripes are only for spacious rooms but narrow stripes can add interest to a small room without looking too pompous. Painting stripes is difficult and most striped wallpapers are too fussy for small homes, but one way of providing stripes very cheaply is to stick coloured tape at regular intervals vertically on the wall. Use a plumb line and a measuring tape to make sure you get them vertical and the right distance apart.

Another treatment for these rooms is to use one of the decorative paint finishes such as stippling, or to conceal the shape of the room with storage.

Tall, narrow rooms

Horizontal stripes can be effective in tall, narrow rooms in seeming to lower the height. A strip of contrasting colour at dado height—86cm (34in) from the floor—is best in rooms over 2.75m (9ft) high; any room with a lower ceiling height might look like a railway carriage if the walls are divided in this way. The strip need not be simply a painted colour, but could be a wooden dado rail. This can be painted in a matching colour to the wall, a contrasting colour or the same colour as the rest of the woodwork. The wall below the dado can be painted either a contrasting colour, or a darker or lighter tone. You can make a narrow room appear wider by using a stronger or a paler colour on the lower part of the walls, say from picture or dado level down.

Use friezes or stencils in strips to divide the wall at picture rail or dado height, or even at skirting height. Try

to keep them simple and bold, so that the effect is not too fussy. A simple geometric pattern may be easier to live with in the long run than whimsical bows and baskets, which can add extra clutter to an already busy room.

By painting a high ceiling in a darker colour, picking out any ceiling mouldings, roses, cornices and so on in white or other contrasting pale colour, you will effectively lower the impression of height. Warm colours such as reds and oranges will also appear to bring the ceiling nearer. It may also help to have a dark-coloured floor because the two dark areas will appear to meet each other and thus shorten the apparent height of the walls.

Bright colours, used very simply, create an interesting space in a square kitchen.

To make the space look wider, paint one wall a different colour to the others or use mirrors to make the narrow space look wider. Two or three mirrors can create a wonderful *trompe l'oeil* effect of space.

Low ceilings

Use vertical stripes for walls, which will help to 'push' the ceiling up, paint the ceiling paler than the walls and keep the flooring pale. If the room has low beams, leave them as natural wood if they are in good condition and paint the plaster between them a pale colour—this is an instance when white is best. Ugly beams can be boxed in with pine or painted the same colour as the ceiling so that they appear to merge into it.

Narrow halls, passages, staircase walls

A decorative paint technique such as dragging will give the walls a three-dimensional quality and create interest. Reflect this finish in large mirrors.

USING PAINT TO BRING OUT THE BEST

Sunny, light rooms

Very sunny, bright rooms with plenty of light coming in through the windows can be decorated in cool colours because the daylight will automatically bring the colour to life. In most homes, the upstairs rooms receive more light than the downstairs ones, which may be screened by trees, neighbouring buildings or blank walls.

Architectural details

Pick out good architectural features in white or a positive colour and really make the most of them. They can become noticeable and pleasing features of a room if the eye is attracted to them. Architraving, arches, alcoves, banisters and panelling can all be given character by careful choice of paint.

Draw attention to a pleasant view—a pretty garden, an attractive roof or townscape, or even an enclosed courtyard—by making the window into a 'picture frame'. You can paint it to look like an actual frame or just give it a solid colour in contrast to the walls. Comfortable seating which faces the window and looks outwards will make sense of this treatment.

It is usual to choose a matt paint for walls and a gloss paint for woodwork, but matt paint can be used for the woodwork as well. Eggshell and even emulsion paints are washable nowadays so there is no need to paint the woodwork in a gloss paint. The kitchen and bathroom will also look much less institutional if given a matt rather than a gloss finish.

DECORATIVE PAINT TECHNIQUES

Effective paint finishes can be produced very simply by using two coats of paint, the first one in a slightly darker or paler shade than the second. Various different effects can be produced depending on the type of paint you use, your choice of colours and how you apply the paint. The thing to remember is that there are no hard-and-fast rules and no 'right' or 'wrong' way. Be adventurous, be prepared to experiment and try again if you don't like the result first time.

Here we shall follow the techniques used by two households, one using water-based paints and the other oil-based paints. Once you have got the idea, you can adapt these two techniques to achieve other finishes.

There is a big difference between the effects you can achieve with water-based paints and those achieved with oil-based paints. Oil paints are brighter and clearer in tone because they reflect the light; water-based paints, which include artists' watercolours (gouache), emulsion paints and poster paints, give a much softer, almost faded effect because they absorb the light.

Wash the walls thoroughly before you begin, as you would before any painting job. It should not be necessary to seal a water-based paint finish but, if you really want to, use a matt glaze.

Opposite page This kitchen-dining room was colour-washed in water-based paints, as described on pages 16–17. The woodwork was given the same treatment. Note the high shelf for decorative storage.

The sun-faded look using water-based paint

The paint colour shown in the illustration on page 15 was inspired by some plaster found behind a bookcase. The owners liked the terracotta colour, which reminded them of sunny Italian cafés, and tried to reproduce it as faithfully as possible. They did not want to overdo the 'distressed' side of the technique, feeling that a room which already had a lot going on in it, namely a dual-purpose kitchen-living room (with a baby), should not be too fussy.

1 Achieving the right colour   To get the faded look, you need to use two different paint mixtures and techniques. The first coat is a plain coat of your base colour. Don't underestimate the time needed to find a colour you like. First, look in books and magazines and at your own walls and spaces until you have a clear idea in your head of the colour scheme you want. It is a good idea to paint a simple picture of the room with the walls and ceilings coloured as you want them. With this clear idea on paper, you will recognize the colours when you eventually get them right.

If you are lucky you may find a tin of the right colour paint straight off, without any mixing needed. It is more likely, however, that you will need to do some mixing before you are satisfied.

Once you have achieved the colour for the base coat, you need a very watery wash to paint over it. This will tone down the base colour and give a subtle two-tone effect.

2 Mixing the base coat   The base coat should be mainly emulsion paint with artists' watercolours (gouache) mixed in to get the final result. It is best to use emulsion paint as a base, because this will 'fix' the gouache colour you add to it. Choose an emulsion as near to your ideal colour as you can find. If you start with white emulsion, you will need much more gouache than if you start with a colour nearer to what you want and gouache is quite costly for a small tube. You can use poster paint instead of gouache, which is the cheaper option, but the colours are not quite as good.

Put a blob of the emulsion you have chosen (always the same amount) onto a saucer. Then add a small squeeze of colour from a tube of gouache or poster paint and mix it until you think you have the colour you want. Don't be too timid; squeeze a good dollop out and see what happens. Use about six saucers, with different amounts of colour in each. Number the saucers, and note the names of the colours and the amounts of paint used in each. As you finish mixing each colour, paint a small patch on the wall and let it dry; number the patches painted on the wall to correspond to each saucer. When the paint has dried, it will almost certainly not be the same as when wet and you may have to do some more mixing before the colour turns out as you wish.

The colour in the photograph was created using Indian red, burnt sienna and burnt umber, which together produced a rather dull, quite dark terracotta shade.

When the test pieces are absolutely dry, test your wash colour over them before you make any final judgements and before you do the painting proper. In this room, several washes, based on a browny grey, were tried which all made the paint quite a lot darker so in the end a much paler base coat was chosen than had originally been intended.

Remember to write down everything as you go because it is so easy to forget. You may have to mix as many as 12 test saucers before you are satisfied with the colour. At this stage, you may be tempted to leave the colour as it is and forget about the wash, but the wash will tone down colours which are too 'candyfloss' and will make most colours more interesting without spoiling them.

When you have decided which colours you like, and with your saucer and notes as a guide, mix all the paint you will need before you begin painting the walls because it will be impossible to get the same result again.

Others colours you can try for the base coat:
Mediterranean blue-green: cobalt blue, ultramarine, yellow ochre, a little black and a little white
grey: black and white, with a little ultramarine or red

3 Mixing the wash A wash is mostly water so quantities will be about half a bucket of water to a spoonful of emulsion, plus a squeeze or two of dark brown gouache. The finished preparation should look like a muddy puddle.

4 The painting Paint the wall first with the base coat, just as you would normally, using an ordinary paint-brush. When it is quite dry apply the wash coat, using a car-cleaning sponge. Work with broad sweeps of your arm to add scarcely perceptible patterns of colour onto the base coat. Do not be worried about any unevenness, that is part of the charm. The important thing is to work quickly and to do each wall in one go because the mixture dries very quickly, and to get right into the corners.

This 'smoky' finish removed from the walls in our photograph the rather sugary sweetness which the pale pink and green started off with. In this case, three washes were used; if you use more than one, let the paint dry before applying the next coat.

5 The woodwork Exactly the same technique was used for the woodwork, with greeny blue gouache to get the right shade for the emulsion but much the same colour for the wash. Use a smaller paintbrush and a cutting-in brush, which helps to get into the corners of the windows.

An exotic finish using oil-based paint

Many decorative techniques can be created with oil paints. Some are quite complicated and require professional expertise, but it is not difficult to achieve the effects shown here and with a little practice more complicated finishes can be achieved.

The idea is exactly the same as with water-based paints: a base coat is covered with a second, almost transparent coat, the difference being that oil paints reflect the light and in consequence give a much more positive effect.

The basic technique is to apply a coat of paint to the

wall and, when it is dry, to use a brush to apply a coat of coloured glaze over it. The base coat in this case was an eggshell gloss and the glaze was a readymade formula (available clear or tinted). The colour was built up using three different-coloured tubes of artists' oils. You can also use water-based vinyl silk paint for the base paint with water-based techniques, and this is cheaper than a gloss base.

1 The base coat To get a green, mottled effect, as in this kitchen, the walls were painted with a base coat of sky blue eggshell emulsion. This is rather cold as a

This rough kitchen wall has been given a two-tone gloss finish, using the technique described on pages 17–18.

finished colour for most rooms, so green was chosen as the glaze colour to make it a little warmer. You can alter the colour of the base paint by adding small quantities of universal stainers; you start off with a warmer colour, but you may lose some of the subtle three-dimensional quality. Try small variations, painting small patches on hidden areas of the wall until you find one you like. As in the water-based painting, make notes so that you can mix up a larger amount when you have decided on a colour.

2 The glaze   This is equivalent to the wash in the water-based paint technique. Use clear, 'flat' varnish and tint it with green universal stainer. Paint stainer is very concentrated so one pack or tube will probably be more than enough. Try the glaze coat over the patches of base coat you have tested until the colour seems right.

Add a bottle of Terebine paint dryer and mix well before you start painting. Mix the glaze in a metal container such as an old paint can, not plastic.

For painting the glaze, use a large, old brush or a painter's dust brush with spaced bristles, but not a good-quality paintbrush. You want the uneven finish that an old brush will give you. A pasting brush is good and extremely cheap. As with the water-based paint technique, keep your brush moving. Odd imperfections and unevennesses will look perfectly acceptable, but the varnish dries very quickly so make sure you don't keep going over the same area or you will leave heavy patches of colour in one place. Use turpentine or white spirit to keep the varnish from building up too much on the brush. Don't use a roller, which would seize up after a few minutes.

You can paint with wide sweeps of the arm to create a positive pattern, small wrist movements to give a more curved pattern effect or up-and-down strokes to give vertical lines, but once you have chosen a way of working, stick to it.

3 Variations   The hall shown on page 8 was painted with an eggshell emulsion in marigold (a very deep eggyolk yellow). Flat varnish was used for the glaze, with red, dark brown and ochre universal stainers and paint dryer to produce a really glowing red. Blobs of a dark brown glaze, mixed very thickly, were added at fairly regular intervals and painted in with quick up-and-down strokes to get darker strokes, giving an intriguing and subtle effect and toning down the red. This extra colour can be quite a labour because it has to be added very quickly during the glazing, so be warned.

You can drag a second colour over an existing wall colour, completely changing the quality of the first colour as a very inexpensive way of achieving an interesting effect. Dragged colour always ends up paler when it is dry, so be bold and start with a deeper colour than the one you want to end up with. Any colour can be dragged—the easiest way is to stick to two similar colours, the top one being a tone or two paler or darker than the base coat. Advice for beginners is usually to start with a pale colour and make it brighter with the glaze, but with oil paints you can equally well start with a bright colour and tone it down.

4 The woodwork   Use the same technique as for the walls. If the existing paintwork is in good condition you can glaze straight onto it without bothering with a base coat, but you must make sure the existing paint is clean. In this case, the glaze was painted over the original magnolia. Use yellow ochre stain in the varnish to get the colour in our picture, or choose another colour. Drag the glaze slowly over the paintwork with an old brush.

When you become more confident you can try contrasting colours, but they should always be subtle, not deep colours. Colours you could try are orangey yellow over yellow; deep brick red over pale brick red; or dark grey over light grey.

PAINTING A SINGLE COLOUR

- Be sure to buy enough paint because it is almost impossible to match the colour exactly if you have to go back for more.

- Pale paint over dark paint will need more coats.

- Walls should be dry, smooth and clean before decorating.

- Include radiators in your design—don't always leave them white unless white is part of your scheme.

Measuring

Measure the height and width of each wall and multiply the two figures to get the square area, eg, a wall measuring 3 x 3.5m (10 x 11½ft) has a total area of 10.5 sq m (115 sq ft). Add up the wall measurements for the total area. Include windows and doorways as part of the surface but leave out any skirtings or friezes. Don't forget to include alcoves and chimneys, and the insides of cupboards.

Quantities

The amount of paint you need will depend on how porous the wall surface is, the type and brand of paint and how many coats you need to apply. Here is a general guide to the areas that different kinds of paint can be expected to cover:

Walls (coverage per litre)
emulsion (thin with water) 15 sq m (18 sq yd)
non-drip emulsion 14 sq m (16¾ sq yd)
oil-based silk finish 12 sq m (14½ sq yd)
gloss (thin with white spirit) 17 sq m (20¼ sq yd)
non-drip gloss 12 sq m (14½ sq yd)
polythene (for pipes, metal window frames and radiators; thin with white spirit) 14–18 sq m (16¼–22¼ sq yd)

Ceilings   Multiply the widths of two adjacent walls. Calculate the ceiling area of the alcoves in the same way and add this to the ceiling measurement.

Windows and doors   Measure the width and height as for the walls and multiply.

Skirtings   For the total skirting area, multiply the total length of the skirting by the height of the boards.

White walls give the feeling of space in a narrow bathroom. Opaque panels on the lowered ceiling give soft but effective light.

Various paint effects:

Far left Blue emulsion was pressed onto the white base coat, using a natural sponge.

Top left Orangey-apricot emulsion was rag-rolled and a second, yellow rag-rolling applied when the first was dry.

Below left For subtle stripes, dab paint of various tones of one colour at the top of the wall then drag them down, dipping the brush in water to keep the paint runny.

Right Extra-tough green gloss paint with a matt metallic sheen was diluted with white spirit and painted over the base coat, then sprayed with water.

Storage Galore

Storage space should look decorative and be carefully thought through. Disciplined planning can produce efficient storage in the smallest of homes without impinging on the usable space.

In this picture, the sloping ceiling of designer Graham Hopewell's London flat contains tapered fitted bookcases and a large painting, as well as a low shelf/seat with storage below.

The key to ordered living is to have enough of the right kind of storage. Some sort of order is absolutely essential if you are not going to be in trouble because you can't find the electricity bill, your child's half-term dates, the skirt you want to wear for an important meeting or the car keys. You may brighten and enliven a space as much as you like, but if you haven't got the storage to keep all your belongings where you can find them and where you can easily get at them, you will live in a state of constant chaos and anxiety.

Different kinds of objects require different kinds of storage. Books should be kept upright, where the titles can be seen, not too tightly packed together and on shelves which are deep enough so that they don't sit on the edge but not so deep that they keep being pushed to the back. Some clothes must have hanging space and shoes should have their own shelves or pockets. Letters and papers need some sort of filing system, even if it is just a row of shoeboxes, and toys should be kept in drawers or boxes where they can be divided into type and size so they don't get hidden or crushed under larger objects. Even pictures (for which storage and display are the same thing) need a wall, and decorative objects should have some sort of cabinet or shelf where they can be a focal point. Above all, everything should have its own place and not have to be stuffed into a communal cupboard where it may get lost or damaged.

You should not have to climb or stoop to get at things you need frequently, but things you only use once a year can be tucked away under the bed or in high places. The first thing is to make a list of the different kinds of objects you own, and then to decide what sort of storage would be most suitable for each and where you can provide it.

OPEN SHELVING

In most homes, some form of open shelving is going to play a large part. Open shelving provides flexible storage space and allows items to be recognized and reached quickly. It also gives a greater feeling of space than closed cupboards, which reduce the dimensions of a room. There are many different forms of open shelving, from basic metal uprights and individual brackets, whose height can be adjusted at will, to simple shelves on brackets or free-standing shelves, which have the advantage that they are easy to take with you if you ever want to move home.

When you are putting up shelves, consider the heights and depths of the various things you want to put on them and try to see that similar-sized items go on the same shelf. If the shelving is compact and well organized, space is not wasted by putting an enormously tall atlas next to the crime paperbacks.

There are various makes of upright-and-bracket systems available in white or bright primary colours which can be made part of the decor. These were adapted originally from office storage systems but are now available in most household stores. They are sturdy and robust; the brackets vary in size from those that will take narrow shelves for spice jars to very long ones which will take a shelf deep enough to act as a desk. A strip of wood along the edge will give a more solid appearance, as though the shelf were made of solid wood.

The shelves must be thick enough and the uprights close enough to support the weight of whatever you wish to put on them (see page 36). Open shelves in a narrow kitchen can make it seem much more spacious than if they were boxed off by cupboard doors, but they are nearly always more satisfactory if they have sides. These may be an integral part of a shelving system, or may be provided by the walls of an alcove, or even fixed to the shelves when they are in place. An upright-and-bracket system can be made to look built in if it is finished off top and bottom with architraving.

Olive green or grey metal office shelving is often available secondhand. Although it may not look very beautiful at first, it can be painted with lacquer in some bright, cheerful colour and by the time it is covered with objects is quite attractive in the right environment,

Left This little dresser (only 79cm/32in wide x 20cm/8in deep) is made up of a cupboard unit with a shelf unit above. It provides an attractive answer to a wall squeezed between doors, which would otherwise be too small to be useful.

Make the most of hanging storage. This wall is too close to the door for shelves or cupboards, but is exactly right for hanging a folding chair.

Right Free-standing shelves have a sculptural quality in this flat, where they house books, sculpture and other objects. They can be added to when necessary to cover more of the wall.

particularly in a modern 'high-tech' home or in the office of somebody who works at home. This sort of shelving will also suit an older child who wants to store models and model-making equipment, computer equipment and a whole lot of other untidy paraphernalia. It may not look elegant but it can at least look cheerful and businesslike. If the door opens too close to the wall to leave room for shelves, perhaps you could fit in a narrow set; a surprising number of books can be stored in a narrow, columnar bookcase.

Shelves do not have to be custom-built or tailor-made or wall-to-wall. Antique shops and pine shops often sell small one-off units which can provide storage for books and objects, with the advantage of acting as small wall sculptures at the same time.

Sets of small shelves can be the perfect place to display items which would otherwise get lost amongst the plethora of belongings in most homes. Free-standing shelves and folding shelves are available in pine shops, do-it-yourself shops and superstores. They are often designed so that they stack, providing a very flexible answer to miscellaneous storage needs. They are usually fairly unassuming and will merge satisfactorily into the background and so go with a number of furnishing styles. They can be slotted in between other pieces of furniture, will hold a multitude of games, books, boxes, toys or box files, and can be easily folded up or dismantled so that you can take them with you if you move or swop them around when your storage needs a change. They are particularly convenient for furnished apartments.

BOXES

Divided shelving is more decorative and possibly more practical than simple shelves. One way to achieve it is a series of boxes, fixed to the wall by brackets, which frame the objects inside them. Because there are no doors, their presence will not diminish the size of the room since you can see through them to the wall at the back. This

WHERE TO PUT SHELVES

One obvious place to put shelves is in an alcove, perhaps one created by a chimneybreast. The advantage of alcoves for bookshelves is that the books are contained by the side walls, which gives them an orderly look. Alcoves need not be filled completely with shelves and look elegant if the lower third is filled with narrow shelves for, say, CD or tape storage, with the space above devoted to something purely decorative such as a painting or a beautifully framed mirror.

There are many other opportunities for providing shelving space. If there is no chimneybreast, bookcases can be fitted on either side of a window. This helps to frame the window and occupies space that is otherwise often unused. The shelves will jut out into the room below the window but you can turn this to advantage, if the window is the right height, by continuing the shelves under the window or building a window seat under it, with shelves under that, so that the whole wall becomes a 'library' with the window as its central feature. A foam cushion covered with an attractive fabric, sewn and piped or simply fixed in place with a staple gun, will make this a comfortable place to sit and read or sew, or gaze out of the window.

Shelves can be put over radiators, partly to direct the warm air into the room rather than allowing it to escape up to the ceiling and partly to give a little extra shelf space, if only for a vase of flowers. It may be possible to place a narrow table so that one end is over a radiator, or a narrow console table or sideboard could be placed with two narrow radiators under each side. The whole of one wall will then not be dedicated to a radiator and will be that much more versatile.

Try a bit of brainstorming and imagine shelves in every possible corner of the house. Many places will not be practical or desirable, but you will have thought about all the possibilities and some unlikely ideas may turn out to be useful. For example, if you have a window looking out onto a miserable view, which you don't rely on to light the

Left Corner shelves use an

otherwise wasted space.

Above A purpose-built storage

unit for pans.

sort of storage needs careful planning, but when well worked out it can be arranged to house decorative objects, books, games, writing equipment, the home office, in fact most things used in day-to-day living. It is particularly suitable for people who collect things and have a great many objects they wish to display.

The boxes can be different in height and width, but look most co-ordinated if they are all the same depth, otherwise the effect can become a bit of a jumble.

Left This tiny cottage shares a chimney with the house next door, leaving an unusually narrow alcove which has been fitted with narrow shelves—ideal for storing food and spice jars and china.

Right The attractive treatment of this alcove makes a display of CDs and china and allows space for a painting, rather than fitting shelves all the way up the wall. The CD and record player are stored at a low level where they are unobtrusive.

room, span it with glass shelves on which you can grow houseplants or display coloured glass.

Shelves can be invaluable in a passageway or hall, or even on a stair landing where pieces of furniture would dwarf the space. Rather than cover a whole wall, create a tall, narrow section which will not dominate the whole space, making the bottom shelves somewhat wider to hold thrown-down gloves, keys and letters; or create a long, low set of shelves, running along the whole length of the hallway, rather like a console table, but with useful shelves underneath. The top shelf will act as a table for post.

If the room is high, don't waste that height but put a shelf close to the ceiling to hold special china. This will give the impression of a decorative frieze as well as providing useful storage; it is a good substitute for stencilling, which looks charming but uses up space rather than creating it. Nail a thin sliver of wood towards the back of the shelf to support plates.

The easiest way of dealing with shelves round a deep-set window is probably to use one of the upright-and-bracket systems available. The bookcase sides can be nailed onto the shelves after you have adjusted the latter to your satisfaction. If you think you may want to move the shelves again later, fit adjustable strips to the inside and fix the shelves to these. A window seat can be made from chipboard or medium-density fibreboard (MDF) and covered with foam cushions.

In a bathroom, where there is often a lot of wasted wall space, you can fit a narrow shelf all round the room, just wide enough to hold jars and bottles and remove them from the windowsill where they are always getting in the way of curtains.

There is often a blind space directly above a doorway where a wider shelf could be fixed to store magazines, family memorabilia and other bits and pieces which you don't want to throw out, but which you aren't actually going to do anything with.

Steep, narrow stairs conceal dark caverns of unused space which can be opened up to take shelving. It is

usually quite easy to remove the wall next to the stairs, which is unlikely to be a retaining wall (although, if in doubt, get advice). You can shelve and decorate the extra space as part of the main room. There may be enough room for a noticeboard on the opposite wall to the stairs. This space can be treated as if it were an alcove, and given a decorative character of its own, as well as providing substantial opportunities for storage (see page 39).

HANGING STORAGE

Never underestimate the importance of hanging things up. Coats, jackets, umbrellas and hats all need to be accounted for and most people have several of each, so one or two hooks in the entrance hall are really not going to be enough.

An ideal solution is the Shaker idea of a wooden strip with wooden pegs which runs right round the wall at shoulder height (see page 82). A simpler version is a

Left *The wooden fascia board holds electric plugs at a convenient height. Kitchen knives slot safely into the back of the worktop.*

wooden batten with cuphooks or other hooks screwed into it. This will hold an endless number of outdoor items (tennis rackets and so on), and even equipment such as a broom or vacuum cleaner.

In the kitchen, a metal rail fixed below the ceiling above the cooker and worktop and hung with butcher's hooks will hold any number of utensils otherwise floundering about in unnecessary cupboards. It should be positioned so that the utensils are not hanging so low that they will brain you as you stir the soup, and not so high that you need a stepladder to get them down.

Cuphooks are the time-honoured way of storing things

with handles, such as cups, mugs and jugs. Don't choose the smallest hooks but get generous-sized ones which will take big, fat handles, and set them far enough apart so that things won't knock into each other when they are hanging at an angle.

FURNITURE THAT FOLDS

Folding chairs and tables are absolutely invaluable in a small home. Directors' chairs and other folding chairs can be hung on the wall, Shaker-style. Some folding furniture comes with its own hanging knob or hook and looks very decorative hanging up as a piece of abstract sculpture. Card tables, decorators' tables and tables with extra leaves are all worth considering. They can be used for anything from Christmas dinner for 20 to playing games or doing jigsaw puzzles.

CUPBOARDS

In small spaces, cupboards are best kept low. Doors at head height can open to hit you on the temple if you stand too close to them, but low cupboards (perhaps with a seat on top and shelving above) are useful for concealing untidy items such as sewing or knitting equipment and give a 'finished' appearance to a room. If the doors are panelled and the door handles brass or ceramic, they look very elegant in traditional buildings; simple metal handles will complement more modern interiors.

Cupboard organization

Hanging on two levels is a good idea for short shirts and jackets. Wire-basket drawers can be fitted inside wardrobes to hold small items such as socks, ties, scarves and belts.

Well-planned wire storage in kitchen cupboards can practically double the available space. Wire baskets at

Left Garden trellis lowers the ceiling and provides useful hanging space.

Top right A lot of storage has been achieved in a tiny space. The double-hanging wardrobe is balanced by deep shelves. The bottom shelf acts as a dressing-table.

Right These small stools are designed to fold up and hang on the wall when not in use.

Shelves over radiators have a dual purpose: to encourage the heat into the room, and for storage and display. Here extra shelves extend the storage, which includes a display of plates.

Right A tall, very narrow pull-out unit is one of the most space-saving ways to store food in a small kitchen. It is divided by wire racks into several compartments so that nothing gets lost.

A traditional bentwood hatstand is invaluable for storing coats, scarves and hats in a small bedroom.

the back of a cupboard can be pulled out like drawers, or fitted inside a door for tins or spices. Narrow wire compartments can be hung on the back of cupboard doors to hold jars, tins, cloths, etc.

Rubbish bins whose lids are automatically raised when the cupboard door opens are helpful in a small kitchen.

MISCELLANEOUS STORAGE

No amount of pre-planned storage is going to solve all your storage problems. There are always little items like drawing pins, elastic bands, corks, postage stamps, pens and pencils and computer disks, and medium-sized things like calculators, cameras, film and so on which don't fall into any convenient storage category. It is important to find places for all these, otherwise they become the very things you can't find when you need them most. There are also bulky items—extra blankets, sleeping bags, duvets and pillows for visitors, and the inevitable stepladders, bicycles and pushchairs.

Let's look at the bulky items first. Drawers that pull out from under beds are practical for extra bedclothes. If the bed is tall enough drawers from an old chest-of-drawers will do, but if you are buying a new bed or divan choose one with drawers specially designed to go under it. Large but comparatively narrow items such as bicycles can be hung on a wall. In modern, minimalist homes they can be a decorative element in a living room, but they take up potential storage space which could be used for other items and this idea would not suit everybody's taste. Items which fold up into narrow shapes take up less space when hung than when simply leaned against a wall.

When it comes to the medium-sized items such as calculators and cameras, you can allocate a drawer to a particular type of storage so that cameras, film and boxes of slides will all be found together.

For the little items which are so difficult to organize, mini chests-of-drawers intended for carpenters' nails and screws are excellent for home office use and will take labels, paperclips and other small items which need to be separate and available. Other drawers can hold buttons, thimbles, hooks and eyes, and other sewing equipment.

Filing can be a problem. Paper never looks tidy and gets lost so easily. Specially designed chunky 'household' files with categorized compartments are theoretically the answer, but the pre-ordained categories seldom correspond to those one actually needs and the files usually end up being too small. It may be better to buy box files or even to use shoeboxes for filing. A low filing cabinet may be the answer, where you can store writing paper, envelopes and other office paraphernalia as well as letters. In a room which has to double as an office and a guest room, files can act as low room-dividers and there's a choice of colours to make them less industrial-looking.

Many bits and pieces can be organized into albums. Photographs take up far too much drawer space and are largely wasted because of the trouble of sorting through them. Albums can be lined up in a bookcase, where they look orderly, take up less space and are easy to find. If you keep Christmas cards, postcards, children's paintings and letters, they will be better preserved by being kept in scrapbooks rather than scattered about in cupboards and chests.

A decorative wall of storage,

where a free-standing system

has been chosen to house a

wide range of objects.

PLANNING CHECKLIST

- List your belongings down to the last elastic band and make sure there is a place for them all.

- Position things in convenient places: the filing system near the table you work at, the telephone next to the directories and a table where you can take notes.

- Store all heavy items below shoulder height.

- Fix adjustable shelving in cupboards.

- Put small items (eg spice jars) on special narrow shelves.

- Fit revolving wire baskets in inaccessible corner cupboards.

- Provide pockets or shelves for shoes.

USEFUL STORAGE TRICKS

- Glass jars are practical for small items because you can see what's inside them.

- If you have pans which can be stacked, put up a small plate rack on the wall to take the lids.

- Hang as much as you can: mops, brushes, the vacuum cleaner, the ironing board.

- Put a knife-rack at the back of the worktop or on the wall.

- Use wall pockets for miscellaneous items such as balls of string and household scissors.

- Trim the edge of a shelf with carpet binding tacked at intervals with carpet tacks to leave slots for such things as scissors, wooden spoons, etc.

RECOMMENDED DISTANCES FOR SHELF SUPPORTS

Shelving material	Distance between uprights
15mm ($\frac{5}{8}$in) hardwood	50cm (20in)
18mm ($\frac{1}{4}$in) plywood	80cm (32in)
25mm (1in) plywood	1m (39in)
12mm ($\frac{1}{2}$in) blockboard	45cm (18in)
18mm ($\frac{1}{4}$in) medium-density fibreboard (MDF)	70cm (28in)
15mm ($\frac{1}{8}$in) melamine-covered chipboard	40cm (16in)
18mm ($\frac{3}{4}$in) melamine-covered chipboard	50cm (20in)
32mm (1$\frac{1}{4}$in) melamine-covered chipboard	90cm (36in)
10mm ($\frac{1}{8}$in) glass	70cm (28in)

Making the Most of Space

Space in interiors is much more flexible than people realize and there are many ways, other than the conventional ones, in which it can be used.

These bunk beds, built by designer Ken Baker, are made from slats which fit into specially built slots in the wall. Extra slats on the left turn the bottom bunk into a double bed. See page 39 for other variations.

In today's smaller homes we cannot afford to waste space and it may be useful to rethink some of the spaces we take for granted. Try to visualize your home as an empty box; in your mind's eye, remove all the furniture and consider the space that is left. How might it work better for you? The most important thing is to start with completely flexible ideas.

If the rooms are very tall there are plenty of opportunities to use the height, either by putting shelves up as described in the previous chapter, or by building platforms, bunks or galleries. All over the house there are probably unused spaces which can be exploited. Try to make sure there are no 'dead' places that are difficult to get at—cupboards where you cannot get into the corners, shelves hidden by heavy furniture and so on.

NARROW SPACES

Even in narrow spaces, there are often opportunities to build in shelves or perhaps readjust the layout to create dual-purpose fittings or to store furniture by hanging it when it is not actually being used.

It is sometimes worth sacrificing cupboards or furniture which are theoretically essential in order to give a feeling of space, and finding other storage elsewhere. A narrow hall with ceiling-height cupboards running along its length will make the entrance feel like a rabbit-hole but if you remove those (perhaps replacing them with a long, narrow table or a low chest) you will create a much more spacious entrance. The storage you have sacrificed can be accommodated in other parts of the home with a bit of ingenuity, perhaps under a bed, in an unused area under the stairs or in a garage if you should be lucky enough to own one.

Look for unlikely places to store things. Instead of large cupboards in the hall, try a set of very narrow shelves—without the cupboard doors to make the place feel enclosed. Leave a length of the hall unshelved and install a mirror there to enhance the sense of space.

Left A sturdy platform built above the door of this bedroom holds a double mattress and extra storage.

Top right The bunk beds built by Ken Baker are very versatile. The bunk slats have been removed and placed in the slots directly above to make a desk area.

Below right The top bunk has been removed, leaving a single bed. Two slats fitted into slots at desk height make a narrow bedside table.

Kitchens are often narrow. One way of dealing with this is to have the 'cooking' side and the 'washing' side opposite each other, so that the two activities are kept separate. This works if the two areas are not interrupted by doors. It is often possible to put a small folding table and folding chairs at one end for eating. Measure the space carefully and check that there is room in the working part of the kitchen to open the oven and refrigerator doors comfortably. Make sure you leave enough space so that when you bend to get something out of the oven or a bottom drawer, you can do so without bumping into anything. Include as much work-top space as possible and don't put deep, head-high cupboards where the doors will knock you in the eye when you open them. If the room is very narrow, it is better to have open shelves which are slightly less deep than cupboards would be. Leave a narrow gap between the kitchen units to hold trays, which get in the way.

UNDER THE STAIRS

Look at the space under the stairs. It takes different forms and shapes, depending on which way the stairs run and how wide they are, but it is nearly always under-used. Would the space be more useful if it were not boxed in but became part of the main space, whether in the hall or the living room? Is it deep enough to take a desk, or a chair and telephone table? If the staircase is in the kitchen, will the refrigerator fit under it? Or would the run of kitchen fittings and cupboards carry right on under it so that it becomes part of the main kitchen? Would it be better to fit the staircase space with cupboards and drawers rather than opening up the whole space?

Is it big enough to get a small shower room into, or a tiny bath? Very small baths, slightly deeper than normal for sitting in seats, are available and can be fitted under a staircase if there is enough headroom and the plumbing can be organized without too much expense. An oval bath takes up much less space than a conventional one and can be angled to fit very narrow rooms. If you can bear to give up the idea of a bath altogether, a luxurious shower cubicle can be installed in a very small space.

If the stairs slope quite steeply, it may be possible to put a lavatory under the lower part so that when standing there will be plenty of headroom and when sitting, closer to the slope, there will be still be headroom. A small basin is all that is necessary in an understairs loo. Tiny spaces such as these can be made attractive with pretty ceramic tiles and fitted cupboards can provide extra storage for shoe-cleaning equipment, extra toilet rolls, etc. There may even be room to house the washing machine under a shelf in a downstairs cloakroom, alongside the outdoor boots. This would mean that the space needs to be near another bathroom or the kitchen, so that it will not be too expensive to run the pipes to it and so that drainage is also nearby.

It is possible to remove the concealing wall from the stairs so that the whole staircase becomes part of the neighbouring room. Even so, it can be a separate part, providing an area for telephoning, study or storage. A wooden staircase with elegant banisters would complement an antique desk and, with a set of bookshelves, would become an efficient and workable office space without encroaching on the main living area. In a ground-floor flat, a tiny but workmanlike kitchen can sometimes be opened out under the taller part of the house's main staircase, extending as an alcove from the living room. When a kitchen is as tiny as this, it must be very well planned and thought out. Such a kitchen would suit a single person. What is usually lacking is worktop space but this can often be provided by the dining table.

WHOLE-WALL STORAGE

There are many different ways of approaching storage which is to cover a whole wall, apart from the easy, good-looking and straightforward ranges of shelving mentioned in the last chapter.

One way is to build in clothes cupboards at each end of the wall, creating an alcove between them which adds to the sense of space in a square room and can hold a chest-of-drawers and a mirror or shelves above it. Louvred doors make this an ideal bedroom solution. Another way of using the complete wall is to divide it up into modular storage and have cupboard doors with finger-holes instead of handles. This gives a whole wallful of storage and still leaves a flat wall surface on which you can hang pictures and prints. It reduces the dimensions of the room, but will leave you with uncluttered wall surfaces.

Above and right To make the most of the garden, this kitchen/living room has a glass 'wall'. Everything needed for cooking and eating is contained in the built-in dresser.

This fridge-freezer has cleverly been tucked under the open staircase.

Under this sloping bathroom ceiling, designer Ken Baker has created a built-in area for the washing machine.

In a kitchen, a whole wall can be turned into a giant, made-to-measure farmhouse dresser, to hold the complete china and cooking equipment for the household. Leave a gap between the end of the dresser and the wall so that you can put a butcher's block there, or keep the vacuum cleaner or any other odd things you want to store out of the way behind a curtain. Partition the shelving to make it both stronger and more decorative, and work out beforehand what your priorities for storage are: if you have a lot of glasses, allow shelves the right size for those; if you have more pans, leave a space on top of the dresser where they can stand within reach but out of the way.

Screw-in cuphooks are always useful for mugs, cups and jugs, and a thin metal bar at the back of the dresser can be used to hang kitchen implements where you can get at them easily. When dressers were first used, they were built for practicality and the householder knew exactly what each surface and hook was for: 'a place for everything and everything in its place'. It is worth making lists and sketches to be absolutely sure that your dresser is right for you.

In a small bedroom, you could give the whole of one wall to storage but make it deep enough to take clothes hangers—53cm (21in) is required to take the width of a coathanger. Next to this hanging storage could be equally deep shelves, one at table height to serve as a dressing table. Within the deeper storage, narrower shelves can be used for make-up and hairdressing equipment, jewellery and so on. Even though such storage is deep it looks best if it extends over the whole wall, where it appears to take up less space than a heavy wardrobe squeezed into a corner. If it is all the same depth it gives a co-ordinated feeling; if it is open, rather than enclosed by doors, it makes the space seem larger.

One advantage of having such deep storage is that the dressing-table top can be used as a sewing table or a desk, which will give the room a dual purpose. Bedroom space is sadly wasted if it is relegated simply to going to bed.

This small room has been divided by designer Graham Hopewell to make a bedroom and also a studio/office.

DIVIDING ROOMS

Sometimes by cleverly dividing a room you may be able to give it an extra function, or even two. A largish bedroom can have one end divided off to give you a roomy wardrobe next to a tiny L-shaped bathroom. If the space is very small you may have to install a shower rather than a bath, but an oval bath can be angled to fit a remarkably small space.

Another successful division can be bedroom and office. A sturdy shelving unit will make a good solid 'wall', providing office storage on one side and leaving space for a small guest bedroom on the other. The division need not reach the ceiling, which might create too claustrophobic an atmosphere in a small space.

MAKING THE MOST OF WHAT'S THERE

If built-in furniture already exists and you cannot very well get rid of it, you may be able to move it or use it differently. In most kitchens, the space given to storage and worktop can be reduced if the room is carefully planned to function at its most efficient. A good kitchen table can be a worktop as well as an eating space. A tabletop can be attached to the wall by a hinged leg.

Once again, the interiors of cupboards can be fitted with wire pull-out baskets and trays; hooks can hold cups and jugs, and stacking equipment is a great space-saver. This means that the working part of a kitchen can take up a comparatively small space, leaving room for entertaining as well as humanizing elements such as pictures and prints.

LESS IS BEST

There is a tendency to overfill kitchens with storage cabinets which are not really necessary. In small kitchens these can be claustrophobic, and it may be better to keep cupboards at a low level and to install narrow shelves where they are needed at a higher level. Instead of a large refrigerator and freezer, it may be more space-saving to have two refrigerators or small, separate fridge and freezer units than one monstrous appliance which dominates the whole room. Small appliances also provide more worktop space. The upper wall space can then be used for storing narrow objects such as spice jars, salt and pepper mills, sauce bottles and so on, or for hanging shallow shelving units, knife-racks, storage for kitchen implements and other decorative, hangable items to cheer up the working environment.

USE THE HEIGHT

In many small homes, the height of the rooms is scarcely used but could almost double both the storage and the living potential. For example, it might be possible to create a balcony area in a living room which could be used as workspace, playspace or for visitors to stay overnight. If there is not enough height for that, a built-up platform could provide storage underneath, at the same time giving the room an added dimension.

In a small bedroom, build the bed on top of a 1.2m (4ft) high cupboard. This is just the right height for being able to see out of the window from the bed, an enormous bonus if you have a pretty view. The cupboard underneath will provide useful storage space for quite large objects, anything from clothes to small pieces of furniture, pictures and pieces of equipment which you may not want to throw away but do not need at present. It is also useful for duvets and pillows for guests. A more primitive version would be a bed base resting on two chests-of-drawers. Make the bed base out of slats with a good 12mm ($\frac{1}{2}$in) between them; if you are using solid pieces of board, drill holes to allow the mattress to air. For a 1m (3ft) high bed you won't need a stepladder but you will need a step of some kind. A box-step can hold lightweight objects so that you have no difficulty raising it

This bedroom is only 1.8m (6ft) wide but by building the double bed 1.2m (4ft) off the floor, right across the room, there is a view of the garden from the bed, a large cupboard underneath and generous wardrobe space.

when you want to get into the cupboard. A chest-of-drawers next to the bed, at about the same height, acts as a bedside table.

A tall bed can be curtained off with muslin or pretty cotton print fabric to give the enclosed and private feeling of a four-poster.

ATTICS AND SLOPING ROOFS

Attics make good play areas for older children, who enjoy the secretiveness of enclosed spaces which would be claustrophobic for adults. When converting an attic, remember to insulate it adequately; it may be possible to get a grant for this. Make sure there is a means of escape in case of fire and that any ladder required for getting up to the room is sturdy and solid. If you install low seating round the walls, people will not bump their heads.

ARCHES AND ALCOVES

If you are converting two rooms into one, you can make the connecting arch a very deep one, perhaps as much as 55cm (22in). This will not only provide alcove space for a number of uses, the top will provide a good platform for displaying objects such as sculptures and even plants if there is enough light. In the alcove you can perhaps fit a refrigerator, an extra cupboard, wine-racks or other bulky items which you may have difficulty finding room for elsewhere.

JAPANESE-STYLE LIVING

The Japanese have made an art of living in small spaces, using sliding screens and doors to make their living spaces highly versatile. Sliding partitions can also play a part in saving space in Western households. We have already recognized the value of the futon, and have adopted it as a good-looking means of providing seating during the day and bedding at night. Japanese rooms are low as well as small, so much so that you can often reach up and touch the ceiling. They are mostly absolutely square, with perhaps one recess in the best room. Rooms are divided by sliding partitions or screens consisting of lightweight frames covered with rice paper to let the light through. In a traditional Japanese house the futons are stored in a cupboard during the day, since the Japanese kneel rather than sit and would have no use for a sofa.

Screens in Western homes do not have to be sliding or fitted. Folding screens have been used for centuries to keep out draughts, to provide an element of privacy while people were dressing and as a psychological division between one part of a room and another. Recently they have begun to be popular again. In a room in which several activities take place at the same time, a screen can be used to separate the kitchen-dining area, say, from the main living area. Folding screens can be covered in woven tapestry fabric or in découpage (see page 68). You could also use lace (see page 89) or anything else you think would look good.

Japanese-type *shoji* screens can be bought in shops specializing in futons and other Japanese furniture, but they are very simple to make yourself (see page 50). Use them to cover untidy shelving, to screen a window with an ugly view or as room-dividers. Venetian blinds can also be used to divide a room, but are pulled up rather than folded vertically.

LANDINGS

Those areas at the top of flights of stairs are simply asking to be converted into something useful. Unfortunately, they often open onto a main staircase and are thus draughty and public. All the same, there is no need to waste their tremendous storage potential. Shelving is one obvious answer and books always give a warm,

comfortable feeling. If the space is square and very small, make the shelves just wide enough to hold paperbacks. If you don't have that many books, magazine collections can be housed there or jars, tins, shoebox files, and so on.

If you don't need extra shelves, then the space could be used as hanging storage—something which is often neglected. You can hang folding chairs, tools, sports equipment or even cleaning equipment (see pages 30–31). Objects which seem uncouth when they are flung higgeldy-piggeldy in the bottom of a cupboard can take on an almost sculptural look when hung in a disciplined way on the wall.

Left Two cupboards have been built into a central hall in this flat. A tabletop, attached to battens, is fixed to the wall between them. The alcove thus created is painted in pale colours to maximize the light.

Opposite page This end-of-terrace basement flat is triangular in shape. The bedroom has been squared off and a shower, toilet and basin fitted into the angle. Folding doors take up minimum space.

The arch created by turning this two-room living space into one has been given greater depth across the top and at the sides, providing storage and display space above and new alcoves on either side.

SPACE-SAVING IDEAS

- Visualize bookshelves running right up and over a doorway and down the other side so that they frame the door. It is surprising how attractive this can look and how much can be stored.

- Where normal-sized doors would be cumbersome and get in the way of other doors, furniture or people coming in and out, 'bi-folding' doors (hinged in two halves) take up half the space when opened. Sliding doors can save space too, but they must be well built or they will cause endless problems in opening and closing and will not be soundproof.

- In the bathroom or the kitchen, if you have enough height, you can fix a traditional four-rail drier on a pulley. This gets all the drying out of the way and is very efficient in allowing clothes to air and dry quickly.

- If there is space at the end of the bath, you can install the washing machine and drier in purpose-built housing where they are convenient yet out of the way.

- A small oval bath will fit into a narrow bathroom at an angle. This will immediately release space in the rest of the room for shelves, towel rails, etc.

- Don't take shelves right up to the ceiling because it will make the room feel smaller.

- Move the boiler out of the kitchen and put it in a cupboard in the hall or on a top landing.

- Turn the landing at the top of the stairs into a library space with bookshelves, a comfortable chair and adequate lighting to read by.

- Use the landing as wardrobe space for extra clothes.

- Make a narrow window seem wider by fixing a curtain rod wider that the window. Draw back the curtains only as far as the windowframe so that the edges of the window are concealed, suggesting that it extends farther than it really does.

- Make a short, squat window seem taller by fixing the curtain rod higher than the frame. Fill the space between with a cornice.

- If there is a window not quite in the centre of the wall (typical of back rooms in some 19th-century houses), put an identically sized wooden shutter next to the window which will give the illusion that the window is twice its actual size. Louvred or panelled shutters would be effective in this context.

- In the kitchen, if you have an alcove created by the removal of a large object such as a stove or gas fire, it may be cheaper and more convenient to ignore it completely and to simply run shelves or cupboards right across it. This will give the whole wall a co-ordinated look rather than dividing it.

- Don't necessarily site radiators right in the middle of a wall. Provided the heat is directed towards the room, they can be high or low. They don't need to be a conventional shape either; the only thing wrong with some of the sculptural and beautifully coloured radiators available is that they are so expensive.

- Radiators in the form of towel rails are more expensive but may be worth the extra cost because of their dual function.

MAKING A *SHOJI* SCREEN

Use straight-grained timber to prevent the screen from warping. The outer frame should be thick and the inner pieces slender but fairly deep so that the screen will be quite strong while allowing maximum light to come through the panes.

You will need four pieces for the outer frame and as many narrower pieces for the grid as you need for the size of the screen. The panes should be about 32cm (1ft) square. Use a ruler to measure the space where the screen is to go and if you are cutting the wood yourself, mark it with a pencil. Use a metal square to guide the saw and ensure the joints are square. Everything must be marked and sawn accurately or the screen may end up twisted.

JOINING AND GLUING

Join the pieces with halving-joints, in which a notch as wide as the pieces to be joined is sawn out to the halfway point in each piece. Mark the joints where the inner grid pieces are attached to the outer frame and saw them out. Joints in the inner grid can then be chiselled out between two sawcuts. When everything fits together tightly, apply white woodworking glue to the joints and assemble them carefully.

ATTACHING THE PAPER

When the glue on the frame is dry, attach the paper. If you are going to use the screen in front of a window, you only need to paper one side of it; if it is to divide a room, you should paper both sides. Traditionally 100 per cent handmade mulberry paper is used, which is strong, but you can use a substitute as long as it lets light through. Tracing paper is effective but is very brittle and will soon have to be replaced. Smear white woodworking glue on the wooden strips, roll the paper across and pull it fairly tight. When the glue is dry, spray the paper with water and it will shrink to give a tight, unwrinkled surface. It is sensible to finish by spraying the whole screen with fire-retardant spray, available from theatrical suppliers.

MAKING THE TRACK

To make a track for the screen, you can rout out tracks in the floor or build them up using three pieces of timber pinned or glued together. The floor-level track should be only 3mm ($\frac{1}{8}$in) deep and the ceiling track 6mm ($\frac{1}{4}$in) deep, which will allow you to slot the screen in position. A little wax or talcum powder will ensure that the screen runs smoothly.

The Importance of Lighting

Lighting can completely alter the efficiency and mood of a small home.

This picture shows three different light techniques. General light is provided by a Chinese paper umbrella painted to complement the decor; a simple table lamp casts light down onto the desk, while also pleasantly diffusing it through a paper shade; and a picture light is focused to highlight the painting.

It's one thing to know that good lighting is important in a home but quite another to achieve it. Lighting can be a very technical subject beset with jargon of lumens and wattages, uplighters and downlighters, the confusion of the innumerable types of lightbulbs available and the difficulty of finding light fittings which please and do the right job. But good lighting without the jargon is perfectly possible if you identify what you need it to do and then go and find lamps which do it. There is a short glossary at the end of this chapter to help you understand the most commonly used lighting terms.

Basically you need three types of lighting in the home. The first is 'general' lighting, which enables you to see your way around safely and comfortably; the second is 'task' lighting, for reading and working by, and that includes cooking, sewing, homework, paperwork, wood-work, modelmaking and so on; the third is 'highlighting', which is used to light up sculptures, paintings, flower arrangements or any other aspect of your home you wish to make a feature of.

There is a fourth category and that is 'mood' lighting, whose purpose is to create pools of soft light which help provide an atmosphere of comfort and encourage relaxation and a feeling of calm. Lighting has much more influence pyschologically than many people realize, but if you choose the first three types of lighting carefully they should in themselves be able to provide mood lighting at the same time as doing their other specific jobs. There are various different ways in which to achieve these kinds of lighting and a tour of the home will demonstrate them.

EXPERIMENT FIRST

When you are trying to decide what sort of lights you want and where you should put them, beg or borrow several different lamps and try them out in various parts of the room to see the effect. In spite of the huge variety of lamps available, you can provide varied and flexible lighting with only a few types but you do need to know

Left This tiny kitchen is simply an alcove off the living room. It has taken space from what used to be a passage before the house was converted. The cupboards above and below are quite adequate for a disciplined cook.

Right The wall lights in designer Graham Hopewell's flat give attractive general lighting by reflecting light off the white wall. The sideboard acts as a shelf over the two small radiators, so no valuable wall space is wasted.

what the result will be before committing yourself to actually buying and installing them. Try lamps which direct the light upwards to reflect off the ceiling or walls, or those which direct the light downwards. Although very crude and basic, a workman's clip-on lamp on a long lead is useful to test where a light would be effective.

GENERAL LIGHTING

The purpose of general lighting is to allow you to see where you are and where you are going, and to identify the objects and furniture in a room. It includes lighting for safety and you should ensure that staircases are well lit without casting confusing shadows, and that you can see the whole of a room, including individual pieces of furniture which might be knocked into otherwise.

The best general light is probably daylight. If you have large windows or roof lights, then you have a head start over people who live in dark basements. However, at night you will need some sort of general electric light and the best idea is to keep it simple.

Many people rely on a single central bulb to provide general lighting, but if you find this a bit bleak you can have lights fitted into the ceiling which have adjustable sockets so they can be swivelled to face in different directions: straight down or towards a wall or worktop, as you wish. These are less obtrusive than spotlamps and are effective for providing good general lighting. They are often used as work lights as well, for example, over a kitchen worktop.

Spotlamps (or eyeball lamps) are effective in most parts of the home as general lighting. Spots can be fitted individually or on a special track which holds two or three at a time, angled in different directions. For general lighting, choose a spot bulb with a wide beam because too narrow a beam will only highlight details of the room. In a very small or low room, a spot bulb may glare into people's eyes and a bulb with a silvered end would therefore be preferable.

It may not be necessary for the lighting to be at full strength all the time, particularly when it is combined with other forms of lighting, so it makes sense to have it on a dimmer switch which gives you control over the level of brightness.

Staircases
A step, or even a slight change in level, can cause people to trip if they don't see it so all steps and staircases must be properly lit. A light shining downwards from an eyeball fixture or a spotlamp in the ceiling should cover the whole area. The placing of lights on staircases is

Ken Baker's office is meticulously efficient. Strip lights are concealed behind a batten.

important because the steps and risers must not fall in shadow. A fluorescent tube hidden behind a wooden strip or baffle will light up the individual steps. The effect can be softened by the addition of wall lamps with opaque shades, which emit a diffused light. These give a soft glow, helping to soften the main light and making any shadows less strong. Nowadays you can buy low-voltage fluorescent bulbs which will fit into standard sockets.

Living rooms

In many rooms, general lighting can be provided by lamps directed towards the ceiling, from which the light is reflected back into the whole room. There is a wide choice of standard and wall lamps which cast their light upwards. Low-voltage tungsten-halogen bulbs are coated with a special gas to give a bright, white light when heated up, not unlike daylight. They incorporate transformers and dimmer switches, which makes them very versatile and economical. Modern standard tungsten-halogen uplighters are usually elegant and good-looking, they take up little floor space and one should provide enough lighting for general purposes or for work in a small- to average-sized room.

General lighting can also be provided by wall lamps, which give an attractive, diffused glow by reflecting light off the wall.

TASK LIGHTING

This is lighting for doing a specific job of work which requires you to be able to see clearly. It applies just as much to reading a book in a comfortable armchair as working at a desk or sewing table, or the kitchen worktop. In the kitchen, it is important that clear, shadowless light should fall on the worktop where intricate operations with knives and measuring scales are going on all the time. Spotlamps and eyeball lights can be good here, and so can small striplights fitted under the cupboards or

shelves above the worktop. These give a good working light but are also soft and user-friendly because the light source is concealed and they are low.

Among the most useful task lights are angled lamps which can be directed at will. You can alter them to light up a book or sewing machine, or to move the light from one part of your desk to another.

Floor lamps, or standard lamps, which direct the light downwards make good reading lights, particularly if placed behind an armchair where they give a pleasant 'mood' light in a corner at the same time.

Low-voltage lighting, which came onto the market comparatively recently, can be effective for task lighting. The bulb itself is tiny and the reflectors round it give far more precise optical control than ordinary bulbs. Low-voltage lights operate on a supply of only 12 or 14 volts, much less than the mains voltage supply, and they are a fraction of the size of conventional bulbs. If you want a low-voltage system installed throughout your home, get it done before you do any decorating and remember you will need space for a transformer (probably about the size of a gas or electricity meter). Make sure such a system is on dimmer switches because, small though the bulbs are, they can be very bright; if they are over a dining table, say, you may not want them to be too brilliant.

Task lighting in the bathroom or bedroom, for make-up and hairdressing, can be produced either by strips of small incandescent bulbs, which are practical but cruel, or by small fluorescent strips behind a baffle. Bathroom lights should be specially designed to conform to safety regulations and should either be switched on from outside the bathroom door or operated by a pull cord.

The home office

The home office may be in a room on its own, it may share the kitchen table or a corner of the living room, or it may simply be a wide shelf in a child's room where homework is done. Wherever it is, adequate lighting with no confusing shadows is necessary and similar lighting is required for close work such as modelmaking, sewing or

In this small kitchen, torch spots equipped with electronic transformers are clipped onto a track which doubles as a utensil rack.

Above Ken Baker's kitchen

has angled lamps plugged into

the fascia board, behind which

runs the wiring.

constantly, being dull sometimes and brightly sunny at others, so that the interior lighting would need to be constantly adjusted.

Fluorescent light is used a great deal in large offices because of its white, shadowless quality. In small rooms, however, low-voltage worklamps give a clear, white light which is ideal for working and even an incandescent angled lamp will give a perfectly adequate light.

Lighting should come from above and behind the worker, and should shine on the work without casting shadows or glaring into the eyes. A good form of lighting for a workspace which doubles as a dining table is a rise-and-fall lamp hanging from the ceiling. This can be pulled down low over the table for intimate conversations, raised slightly for reading and writing, and raised still higher to give a more general illumination.

Desk lamps should stand so that the lower edge of the shade is about level with your eyes when you are sitting working. Use a 75 watt or 100 watt incandescent bulb with a reflective (silvered) interior, which concentrates the light and gives the impression of a larger bulb. The most popular lamps among architects, designers and other people who work at desks or drawing boards are angled desk lamps such as an Anglepoise or a lamp called the '2001', which have springs to keep them in place once they have been positioned. The heads are flexible and they can be used as downlighters, shining down on the page, or as uplighters, illuminating the whole of the work area with reflected light from the wall or ceiling. (This is particularly good for computer work.) They are available in table-mounted, clamp or clip-on versions and some are available with floorstands, the head and arm sections simply slotting into whatever base you choose. Their flexibility makes them ideal for small workspaces.

Lighting for home computers

Most computer screens have a poor light output themselves so bright lighting in the room will simply overpower the images on the screen. However, you do

drawing. For all these activities, the lighting requirements remain the same: for close work, you need at least 200 watts of incandescent light (the most common form of lighting, using standard screw or bayonet lightbulbs and rather yellow) or 400 watts of fluorescent light directed onto the work area, with a good general back-up light from elsewhere. You always need sufficient background light to see the room and its contents, otherwise the contrast between the darkness of the room and the brightness of the work area will strain your eyes.

A desk is best placed against the wall rather than in front of the window because light from outside alters

This eating area is lit by a rise-and-fall lamp, which can be raised to light the whole corner area, lowered to provide working light over the table, or lowered again to give intimate dining light.

need some background light because the contrast between a dark room and the words on the screen makes it hard for the eyes to adjust from one to the other and is therefore very tiring. Since light levels from the window vary from hour to hour, you want to be able to adjust the room light to make it as comfortable as possible for you while you work and this is an instance where dimmer switches will help. Desk lamps are sometimes helpful (see page 56).

When you are setting up the lighting for computer work, check that there are no reflections on the screen. What usually happens is that the operator gets so used to reflections that he or she doesn't notice them, but if they do exist they are an extra strain on the eyes and are distracting. If you can see the ceiling fixtures reflected in the corner of the screen or if there are bright spots of glare from the general room lighting, then a dimmer will help to reduce them; better still, alter the lighting in the room or the position of the computer screen so as to eliminate them. Fixed spotlamps and ceiling lights are the least flexible, although spots on a track can be adjusted. If the ceiling is high enough and the room small enough, any ceiling fitting will probably be out of sight of the screen anyway. Shiny objects such as mirrors and glass-covered paintings should not be hung in a computer room.

Remember that lighting is just as important for children's computers as it is for adults, if not more so.

HIGHLIGHTING

Many people have decorative displays of china, glass or other collections, and objects such as copper pans, books and even architectural details can all be highly decorative. To do them justice, they should be well lit so that they stand out from the rest of the room.

There are various ways of highlighting. For pictures, there are special picture lights which are fixed above the picture and shine down on it, leaving the surroundings in shadow. Spotlamps can highlight objects satisfactorily but you need to experiment to make sure the beam falls on the object from the right direction and at the right angle, without glaring into people's eyes. Ceiling tracks are useful if you want several spots on different objects, but again the placing of the track is important so that the spots can be directed without glare.

Glass is most effective lit from behind. Daylight coming through a window gives it a wonderful sparkle and a collection of coloured glass bottles looks spectacular on a windowsill. At night, subdued light at the back will emphasize the colours and reflections in an entirely different way.

Flower arrangements also come to life when lit from behind. A gentle, diffused light will not compete with the flowers but will throw the shapes and colours into relief so that they and their container take on an extra charm.

If you are lighting objects in a glass cabinet, it is best to use small striplights at the back. If you try to shine a light on the cabinet from outside, the reflections in the glass will prevent you from seeing the objects inside.

MOOD LIGHTING

Mood lighting gives each room in the home its particular appeal without making itself obvious. It is best described, perhaps, as pools of light which are there simply to provide a gentle glow or may double up to highlight objects on a small table, or as sculptural shapes in their own right.

One well-known Scandinavian designer refused to have any light above waist height in his living room because at that height the lighting gives a particularly warm and friendly atmosphere. Ceramic bowls with wide fabric shades set on low tables give a friendly glow to corners of the room which might seem too much in shadow. If you decide to have several small lamps, they can be attached to the same wall switch so that they can all be controlled at once.

Work lights need not be enormous to be effective. This cantilevered table lamp can be angled to suit the person working at the desk. Simply turn it off if it causes glare in the computer screen.

A clip-on spotlight is ideal for highlighting treasured possessions. It can be angled or moved whenever you wish.

MIRRORS

There are many uses for mirrors in the home and to create more light is one of the most important. Mirrors not only appear to extend a small area in various directions, they can also almost double the light, giving a completely different feeling to a room which previously seemed rather dark and cavern-like. They should be placed so that they get the benefit of any light from windows.

Mirrors also reflect artificial light. This probably works best if the light is fairly white, so a tungsten-halogen uplighter floor lamp which reflects light off white ceilings and walls will have most effect.

Mirrors can be placed at right angles to each other or opposite one another, creating innumerable reflections all of which add to the amount of light and give the illusion of space.

CHILDREN'S ROOMS

General lighting for young children should be bright and revealing. Children like to make full use of the whole room and all the floor space when they are playing, and they will be encouraged to do so if the room is well lit.

Satisfactory lighting can be provided by a single ceiling pendant with a high-wattage bulb, up to 150 watts, and a pretty but not too obscuring shade. The ubiquitous Japanese globe-shaped paper lampshades are ideal for this, giving a clear but non-glaring light. Many have printed designs specially for children, although the natural white ones give a lovely light. If you do buy one with pictures or some sort of design, check that it lets plenty of clear light through.

All desks in the house should be provided with an adjustable lamp and children's homework areas are no exception. Even before they go to school, children like to paint and draw, cut out, stick, make models and so on, and for all these activities they need good light. Bad light

Many other types of light give this same warm pool of light—corrugated paper tubes, glass bowls filled with light, 'paper bag' or 'kite' lights, and oldfashioned oil-type lamps with glass shades. Wall lamps with opaque shades, which were originally designed to screen candles, are now available in hundreds of different shapes and sizes, some with the light diffused by shades placed in front of the bulb, others directing the light upwards from a sort of half-bowl. These will provide general as well as mood lighting, although they may not provide all the general light necessary for safe progress through the home.

will deter them from doing homework, although neither child nor parent may realize what the problem is.

For older children, it is important that this general light should be boosted by various lights for the different activities they undertake. The smaller the home, the more likely a child will be to sleep, work, play and entertain friends in the one room.

These individual lights should be chosen with care. Take the bed, for example: even very young children like to look at picture books in bed, and older children usually enjoy reading before they go to sleep. A good reading light is essential and if the children are in bunks each bunk should have its own lamp. Young children should have a pull cord and a light fixed to the wall, not one standing on a table which could be knocked over. Alternatively, the light could be switched on and off from the door so that the parent is in control. An older child can have a light which is switched on and off from the bed so that he or she can read before settling down to sleep.

In children's rooms it is most important to plan for safety. There should be absolutely no trailing leads, and nothing easily knocked over or broken. Lamps should be ceiling- or wall-hung, or firmly fixed to the frame of the bed or bunk. When installing sockets, set them at table height so that young crawlers and toddlers won't be tempted to poke their fingers into them. Where floor-level sockets already exist, fit them with clip-on socket covers.

Unfortunately, children are prime targets for badly made goods; if something is pretty enough or advertised enough, a child will want it and it can be hard to say no. However, where lighting is concerned, poor-quality fittings must be absolutely taboo. Metal lamps may be badly insulated and become live; plastic lamps may break or simply fall to pieces. Always look for safety symbols when buying lamps, or buy from reputable manufacturers and retailers. Old fittings, no matter how charming and nostalgic, are a potential danger and there are plenty of new fittings which are safe, fun and inexpensive.

Another very important consideration for children's rooms is a nightlight. Some children find it frightening to be left completely in the dark, but there is a good choice of lamps which just give a dim glow to help them to go to sleep and to comfort them if they wake up in the middle of the night. It doesn't have to be a bright illumination, indeed too bright a light would be disturbing.

Graham Hopewell designed the top floor of his tiny flat to stop short, thus providing skylights over the stairwell and dining area. Globe lamps give a shadowless background light.

GUIDE TO LIGHTBULBS

GLS (General Lighting Service): The standard bulb used for general lighting in pendant, table, floor, wall and ceiling light fittings in most homes. Screw or bayonet base. Available in 40–150 watts, and in mushroom or globe shape.

GLS crown silver: A spot bulb whose front is coated with silver or gold. Used for display. Screw, bayonet or small bayonet base. Available in 40–100 watts.

ISL 80/95: Internally silvered spot bulb used as task lights, downlights, wallwashers and soft-accent lights. Screw or bayonet base. Available in 40–150 watts.

ISL 125: Use as the ISL 80/95. Available in 75–300 watts.

PAR (parabolic reflector lamp): These can be used for floodlighting or spotlighting. All PAR bulbs are made of two pieces of glass fused together: one is the reflector, the other the front lens. The way the lens is patterned determines the beam angle. The lamp can be used out of doors. PAR bulbs are also available in tungsten-halogen versions.

PAR 38: Used for downlights, wallwashers, accent lights and outdoor and patio fittings. Screw base. Available in 75–120 watts, and in flood or spot beam. Other PAR lamps are for more specialist use.

Incandescent tungsten-halogen: Small incandescent bulbs filled with halogen gas. They give a more efficient, whiter light and have a life expectancy of 3000 hours. They are found in many modern table and floor lamps. Any bulbs over 500 watts should be used in a horizontal position. Available in 100–2000 watts.

Incandescent low voltage: All these bulbs operate at under 25 volts and they always need a transformer to lower the voltage from mains voltage. They include **bare lamps**, which are tiny bulbs increasingly used in modern desk and table lamps, and also in track, recessed and accent lights; **PAR 36** have a life of 1500–2500 hours. Some have dichroic reflectors which divert the heat out at the back, making the light beam much colder. Available in 5–1000 watts.

Iridescent: There are many decorative incandescent bulbs on the market which are used for entertainment value rather than the light they produce. Some are candle-shaped, some flicker, some have decorative light-up interiors and others come in lurid colours. They are usually available in low wattages.

Fluorescent tubes: These range from straight tubes to curved tubes, in many sizes and variations of white colour. Available in 35–40 watts.

Miniature fluorescent tubes: These include the **PL**, suitable for halls, which requires control gear in the light fitting (available in 5–12 watts); the **SL**, which has its own small transformer in the tube (available in 18 watts); and the **2D** which, with a special adaptor, can be plugged into an ordinary bayonet-cap socket (available in 16 or 28 watts).

GLOSSARY OF COMMON LIGHTING TERMS

A-lamp (USA): standard lightbulb.
Accent lighting: a narrow beam used to highlight a particularly object or feature.
Ambient lighting: see *General lighting*.
Ampere (*amp*): internationally agreed unit of electric current.

In this elegant flat, a modern Italian glass table lamp provides a sculptural pool of light which silhouettes the vase of flowers and highlights the African masks.

Background lighting: see *General lighting*.

Baffle: a shield attached to a light fitting to prevent glare.

Ballast (or choke): a device to prevent fluorescent tubes from consuming more and more electric current. Usually in a heavy black box.

Bayonet fitting (UK): standard type of bulb base with two ears for attaching a tungsten bulb to a lamp socket.

Beam: the line of light running from the light source to the object, particularly from a reflector bulb or fitting. The beam can be narrow, medium or wide.

Bulb: the glass bubble that protects the light source.

Choke: see *Ballast*.

Circuit: the complete path of an electric current along the supply cables to the light fittings and back to the beginning.

Cold-beam bulb: a type of PAR bulb which greatly reduces the heat of the beam.

Compact fluorescent: a small bulb (eg the Philips PL and SL and the Thorn 2D) which operates on the same principle as the fluorescent tube. Can be used in a wide variety of fittings but cannot be dimmed.

Diffused light: light filtered evenly through a translucent material.

Direct light: light provided directly from a fitting without using a reflector or reflecting off any other surface.

Downlighter: a light fitting that casts the light downwards.

Edison screw: a standard tungsten bulb with a screw for attaching the bulb base to the socket.

Eyeball fitting: a semi-recessed ceiling fitting which can be swivelled in its socket to direct the light at an angle.

Filament: thin wire (usually tungsten) which emits light when heated to incandescence.

Fitting: the housing for a socket and bulb.

Fluorescent: white light in a tubular glass case coated inside with phosphorescent powders. The phosphorus emits light when switched on.

General lighting: low level of light illuminating an area uniformly.

Glare: bright light shining into the eyes.

Incandescent light: yellow light provided by heating tungsten to a temperature at which it glows.

Indirect light: light which is bounced off another surface before reaching its destination.

ISL bulbs: see Guide to lightbulbs, page 63.

Lamp: in the trade this is the term for a bulb, but it is what most people call the light fitting.

Low-voltage bulb: a mini-bulb running on 12 or 24 volts rather than mains voltage. It needs a transformer.

Multi-mirror bulb: a miniature low-voltage bulb with a multi-faceted reflector, used in many modern lamp designs.

PAR: see Guide to lightbulbs, page 63.

Pendant: light fitting which is suspended from the ceiling.

Quartz-halogen: see *Tungsten-halogen*.

R-lamp (USA): see PAR, Guide to lightbulbs, page 63.

Reflector bulb (UK): see PAR, Guide to lightbulbs, page 63.

Shade: a cover for the light source to prevent glare, control light distribution and/or diffuse and colour the light.

Spotlight: a light source producing a directional beam (see Guide to lightbulbs, page 63).

Task light: lighting to work or read by.

Track: insulated fitting in various lengths to which spot (or other) lamps can be fitted.

Transformer: a device to lower the domestic electricity supply from mains voltage to low voltage.

Tungsten: see *Incandescent light*.

Tungsten-halogen: a conventional incandescent filament with the addition of a halogen gas. The gas combines with tungsten to create a brighter light than incandescent on its own and prolongs the life of the bulb.

Tungsten strip light: tungsten light in the form of a tube rather than a bulb, sometimes known as an 'architectural tube'.

Uplighter: a light fitting that casts its light upwards.

Wallwasher: a light fitting that casts a broad swathe of light along and down (or up) a wall.

Watt: unit of power describing the electrical output of a bulb.

Pictures, Frames and Displays

Finding space for decorative possessions may seem difficult in a small home but there are many unusual ways to display objects.

A fireplace is an obvious focus and always attracts attention to the objects arranged around it. Here the narrow mantelshelf can only hold small objects, so larger ones are ranged round the grate.

Pictures and objects on the walls will do wonders to distract the eye from a multitude of decorating sins. Putting up new paintings or prints is the easiest way to give a room an instant facelift, and you can change them round every so often. There is also nothing like a personal collection of china, dolls, telephones or whatever to give your home an individual atmosphere and a focus of interest.

Walls often have untapped display potential and there are many opportunities for exhibition space on existing shelves, corner cabinets and even small tables which will make the most of your favourite objects while still allowing you space to live. Small objects can be displayed in a number of ways, for example, in the tiny wooden compartments of old printing typecases or on miniature shelves.

This chapter suggests some ideas but individual homes and individual people will find new and personal ways to display their possessions.

PICTURES

This includes anything which is flat and either framed or mounted. It could be a piece of embroidery, such as a sampler or a Chinese silk picture, a print, poster, painting, photograph, sketch or portrait, or a collection of cartoons, menus, cigarette cards, postcards, stamps or other ephemera.

Frames

A picture can be framed with or without glass. It is usual to frame oil colours without because the glass interferes with the visual experience of the texture of the paint and can also reflect light from windows, acting as a mirror which conceals the painting rather than reveals it.

Don't be in too much of a hurry to make a choice. A large painting may look best in a frame of dark wood, pale wood or metal, in something plain or something ornate and gilded. Try the picture with different kinds of frame and bear in mind where you want to hang it. You may be surprised to find how attractive it looks in a frame you had not initially thought of. For example, a very small painting sometimes looks good in a large frame, particularly one in which the frame is deeper in the middle so that the painting is pushed forward slightly and thus given a prominence not afforded by its size.

Storing paintings which you have inherited or do not have a place for at present can be a problem. You can take them out of their frames and store them in acid-free tissue paper either flat in a drawer or rolled up in a cardboard tube; use the frame for a picture you *do* want to display. Framing is expensive so this is a sensible cost-saving exercise. Frames can be dismantled and cut down to make smaller frames, or renovated and re-used as they are.

With watercolours, it is normal to place them on a mount before framing. The painting can cover the whole mount or some of the mount may show within the frame. Suit the proportions of the mount to the painting—if the mount is too narrow it can look ungenerous, if too wide it may dominate the painting. In conventional mounting, the margins at the top and sides should be of equal width while the bottom margin should be about 15 per cent wider.

Sandwich framing

Pictures, mounted or not, can be sandwiched between a sheet of glass or clear acrylic and a backing board (see page 73). If you use two sheets of acrylic, you can make a two-way picture to hang in a window or between shelves that are used as a room-divider.

Placing pictures

It is not absolutely necessary to fill up every blank space. An empty wall can be as interesting a feature as a cabinet of china, especially if the rest of your home is full of objects; one bare wall will provide a refreshing contrast. If you have an exquisite small painting or one large, important one, don't be afraid to give it a wall to itself.

Right This very small workman's cottage has little storage space, and imagination was needed to provide extra. A narrow glass-fronted display cabinet fits exactly into the living room opposite the main staircase.

Left Small wooden boxes like this *were once used by printers to hold metal* type. Today they *make attractive display cases for small objects.*

You will still have other walls for the more concentrated treatment which may be necessary if you want to display everything you own.

Group a collection of pictures close together so that they relate to one another or to other objects near them. They may relate in shape and size, in colour, in having identical frames, in dealing with the same subject or in being a 'set' or series of prints. If portraits are included in this group, they will look best facing towards each other or into the centre of the group.

Photographs often look better grouped in this way than displayed individually; seeing them in numbers gives them a strength they would not possess alone. They are normally much smaller than paintings and lack depth of colour and brush-stroke. This is also a good way of making use of photographs which are otherwise so often just left to lie around loose in drawers.

Some small paintings hold their own when displayed individually, but some vanish into non-existence and will gain importance and interest if placed with others. When grouping pictures, it is usually more effective if you leave very little space between them. Grouped pictures can be symmetrical, in which case they should have identical frames, be of identical size and have a shared theme. Symmetry is by no means essential but groups should be balanced. Distribute wide or dark frames among narrower frames and balance one large picture with a number of smaller ones. It is a good idea to plan your arrangement on the floor before you put the pictures on the wall. This will give you a chance to readjust and rearrange them until you feel the result is pleasing.

Do not forget to use walls you might not normally think of for hanging pictures. The bathroom, lavatory and kitchen are usually treated as purely utility rooms and excellent display potential is neglected. If there is condensation (as there may well be in any of these rooms), it would be better to hang some other decoration such as plates which the damp cannot damage. If the room is warm and dry it will certainly benefit from a few pictures.

DÉCOUPAGE

This is a good way to use images which take your fancy but you can't think what to do with them. Cut out photographs from magazines, use wrapping paper, wallpaper, labels, photographs, postcards, posters (or bits of posters) and decorate one wall of a small room. Alternatively, decorate trunks, tabletops, boxes, screens, trays, cupboards, lavatory doors and so on. In the 19th century, when open fires created draughts, screens were common and were often decorated with découpage including specially printed 'scraps', reprints of which are available today. Your design could be completely random or it could have a theme, such as gardens, animals or fashion.

Make sure the surface to be covered is clean and free from grease or polish. Size the surface if necessary. Using wallpaper paste or any suitable clear glue, stick the pictures onto the desired surface and smooth out any bubbles. When the adhesive is thoroughly dry, varnish the whole with at least four coats of an acrylic varnish which will not turn yellow.

MIXING UTILITY WITH DECORATION

A well-stocked kitchen dresser is full of everyday items, anything from jugs and plates to graters and wire salad baskets. People who choose to keep their kitchen equipment on view are usually very particular about what they buy, and will look for things they like or consider to be well designed so that the dresser is an exhibition area as well as a work unit. In the same way, a simple, narrow kitchen shelving unit allows the packaging and labelling of tins, jars and bottles to create their own entertaining and decorative display.

Another example of mixing the practical with the decorative is to intersperse shelves of humdrum objects (folded towels or the family's toys and games) with one or two shelves in the middle set aside for a display of pretty china. The eye will be drawn to this collection and will ignore the rest, particularly if the display shelves are lit from the back by concealed striplights so that the china stands out in a warm glow. Other possibilities are to use the central shelf or shelves for a vase of flowers or a collection of intriguing objects.

Shelves in themselves can be a source of interest, particularly if they are assymetrical and thereby add a shape of their own. Modular shelving systems, which can be built up in various ways, will fit into almost any space. Another way of combining utility and decoration is to place small sets of shelves at random on walls between pictures or prints. Here they will provide space for those small objects which are always difficult to display but which it is a shame to have to relegate to the permanent darkness of chests-of-drawers or the backs of cupboards.

Small, awkwardly shaped alcoves provide a good balance between the useful and the decorative. A tiny alcove can become a highly personal showcase fitted with just two shelves, comparatively wide apart, so that the top shelf can house the music centre (out of reach of young children) while the lower shelf can hold a selection of small prized possessions and perhaps a painting tucked in at the back.

Some restaurants make a feature of their wine collections by fitting wine-racks all around the walls, up the stairs and over the doors. Wine connoisseurs could take a leaf out of their book and use wine-racks as decorative additions to the room. They can be fitted into the alcoves made by a chimneybreast or the alcoves created by building a deep-arched division between one room and another. The simplest wine-rack, filled with bottles, looks exotic.

Some things are awkwardly shaped for storage—umbrellas, walking sticks, ladders, hats, tennis rackets, and so on. Yet all these things together, perhaps with some purely decorative additions such as hand-carved decoy ducks, can look picturesque. It helps if you hang them from something with more character than the

normal nails or screws—try small brass or china cupboard door handles, or coloured cuphooks, combining practicality and interest.

Tools as decoration

One of the most satisfying, though often unconscious, displays is a wall of well-organized tools. This is an easy and worthwhile project for a garage, outhouse, kitchen or spare bedroom, if that is where the work is done. Tools do not have to be heavyduty, for DIY or woodworking; they can also be small-scale, for jewellery-making, or even sewing equipment.

A deep arch has been built over this door to provide a storage and display area.

The monochrome colours of this picture arrangement complement the colours of the cushions and sofa.

back to its rightful place. This is essential for efficient work and to protect sharp tools such as drill bits and screwdrivers by ensuring they are not damaged by other tools in a toolbox.

Even housework equipment can have a decorative quality hung in this way, although it perhaps merits second-class rather than decorative space since there is inevitably something dusty about it.

JEWELLERY

Some of the most decorative objects we own are our jewellery, yet they are the most difficult to store and display. Strings of beads get mixed up with each other and tangled, rings are scratched and earrings become divided as easily as socks so that you can only find one of a pair when you want to wear them. It is worth searching around for different ways to store jewellery because when it is displayed in the open it looks very rich and exotic, and is certainly safer from damage and easier to find.

A row of hooks on the wall over the dressing-table is a simple answer but there are other ideas. A bamboo-framed mirror, where the frame includes small shelves, looks very pretty festooned with beads and bangles. A collection of individual metal hooks attached to painted metal pictures covering a whole wall would make a very intriguing and decorative 'jewellery bank'. A tailor's dummy will carry necklaces, scarves and hats, and a bentwood hatstand will hold feather boas, hats, scarves and dangling strings of beads. Screens can also be useful for draping scarves and jewellery. Stylized 'hands' will hold numerous rings; cut them out of stiff board, paint them and fix them to the wall so that they lean away at the top.

Earrings are especially tricky things to store. A collection of small boxes will do the trick, or you can create a display. Cover a piece of board in fabric (velvet makes a good backdrop), with a little wadding in

If you give over one wall, or a section of a wall, to kitchen utensils there are various ways of hanging them. Horizontal slats fixed on battens with a 1cm (½in) gap between them provide an ornamental base for storing kitchen bits and pieces, using butcher's hooks or bent wire coathangers as hooks. (Wire coathangers can easily be broken and bent with a pair of pliers.) You can create an interesting sculptural effect by hanging saucepans, sieves, ladles and other cooking equipment on the wall, and save any amount of dresser or shelf space.

DIY tools are best hung on pegboard and hooks, with painted silhouettes of each object to ensure each goes between, and hang it on the wall. Loop the earrings on pins stuck into the fabric, and add stray brooches, hatpins, etc.

Once you start thinking of the possibilities, more and more solutions begin to emerge. A pair of antlers or the protruding parts of wooden-framed mirrors all make good hangers for necklaces, and a champagne bottle is ideal for bracelets; spray it gold if you want it to look even more exotic. If you prefer a high-tech look, plastic-coated wire storage units are very practical for jewellery and are also invaluable for keeping track of scarves, ties, socks and gloves.

FLOWERS

Flowers are a wonderful way to decorate a home. They bring life to a monochrome setting and add extra magic to a colourful one. They can be moved around and, especially if carefully lit, give an added dimension to part of a room. Silk or plastic flowers have their place too, in positions where real flowers would not flourish.

COLLECTIONS

The word 'collection' covers a multitude of interests, from photographs in silver frames to lead soldiers, Dinky toys, horse-brasses, antique dolls and Indonesian masks.

Collections are best grouped together, so that the similarities and differences can be appreciated. A collection of dolls looks at home on an armchair but if you don't want to give up a comfortable seat the top of a chest-of-drawers would be a suitable showcase, perhaps with a set of shelves behind for small dolls and dolls' clothes hanging on the wall on either side. A couple of open drawers could hold yet more dolls peeping out and so the chest becomes a complete small exhibition in itself, leaving the lower drawers for family clothes.

Wooden, alabaster and marble eggs, or other similar-sized objects, can be displayed in a basket or a little batch of baskets. Collections of boxes can spread over the house in groups on mantelpieces, small tables and shelves. Small shelves which are ostensibly intended to stand on the floor can be hung on a wall individually or in groups to display smaller items.

One very successful way of displaying collections is on small tables. A round table covered with a floor-length cloth takes up very little space next to an armchair and collections look very decorative with light shining down on them from a table lamp.

There are dressers to suit all spaces and all tastes. This cheerful dresser fits into a comparatively narrow space.

Even small boxes and chests take up space and the storage of jewellery presents a real problem. Here a piece of ethnic embroidery has been used to display a collection of brooches and earrings.

Masks look best hung on a wall, either in a row if they have some unifying quality or haphazardly if they are different sizes and from different parts of the world.

Glass

Empty bottles are usually thrown away, but some bottles have attractive shapes, colours or ornamental moulding which gives them a decorative value. Don't just display one on its own, their charm is in their variety. Rare or precious glass such as old crystal or Lalique pieces can be exhibited separately but they also look better as collections.

Glass needs light behind it to bring out its magical, light-reflective properties so windowsills are the ideal place to display it. Deep sills will hold a collection of different sizes and shapes but it looks best if you limit the colours to, say, blues and blue-greens, or reds and pinky yellows. Glass also looks extra shiny placed in front of a mirror where its reflective qualities are doubled. After dark, place a nightlight or tiny striplight behind the glass at the back of the windowsill.

China

A high shelf running all round a room or entrance hall will show off a collection of china or an antique dinner service. Pairs of plates or platters can be fixed to wire brackets and hung on the wall on either side of a mantelpiece, and individual plates can be hung like paintings wherever they look good. Don't ignore the bathroom and lavatory as possibilities for hanging china. There are often free walls in these rooms which can be greatly brightened by pretty china, which will not be affected by condensation.

PRACTICALITIES

Picture frames

Professional frames are expensive but worth it for valuable pictures. It is also advisable to have a picture professionally framed if the sides are longer than 1m (3ft) because a frame as big as this is difficult for a beginner to handle.

There are various types of framing kit available, offering a choice of assembly, finish and colour, the main drawback being that most of them are comparatively small. One of the cheapest is in the form of an acrylic box with a close-fitting piece of board to hold the picture in place. When finished, this has no visible frame. More sophisticated kits contain pieces of frame, mitred corners and clips, and fastenings to hang the picture from; check whether you have to buy the backing board and glass separately.

Sandwich framing

An alternative to conventional framing is to place the picture between a sheet of board and a sheet of glass or acrylic, and to simply clip the edges together. This is quite easy to do at home because you can get the glass and board cut to size when you buy them and there is no complicated cutting or assembly.

Spring-loaded clips are available from art shops and framers. Clip sizes vary and should suit the thickness of the combined backing board, glass, picture and mount. Metal or plastic mirror clips, sold by glass merchants, ironmongers and DIY shops, can be used as well.

To fit spring clips:

1 Push a spring clip over the backing board on all four edges. Make a pencil mark where the inner edge of the clip meets the board.

2 Measure between the pencil mark and the edge of the board. Draw lines this distance away and parallel to all the edges.

3 Make holes with a bradawl on the lines you have drawn through the smooth side of the board, a quarter of the board's width from each corner.

4 Place the glass, mount and board face down on a cloth. Fit the spring clips so that the inner ends notch into the holes made with the bradawl.

Panel mounting

Cheap prints, labels and other paper ephemera can be mounted directly onto chipboard panels without glass.

1 Cut the panel to the size of the item and smooth the edges with sandpaper.

2 Chamfer the edges with a plane and fill them with a cellulose filler. Rub down with sandpaper when dry.

3 Paint the edges with emulsion. (Black is the most popular colour.)

4 Mount the picture onto the panel, using the 'wet mounting' technique (see below).

Wet mounting   Paper expands when it gets wet, so handle it with extreme care and practise first on something unimportant.

1 Size the cardboard or chipboard backing board with smooth wallpaper paste.

2 When the size is dry, moisten the back of the print with a damp rag then dab with blotting paper or tissues until the print is limp but not wet.

English bone china plates and cups look their best on the dark-stained wood of an antique dresser.

3 Brush a thin coat of wallpaper paste over the back of the print.

4 Lift the pasted print carefully by the top edge. Align the bottom edge with the edges of the backing.

5 Lower the print onto the board as evenly as you can.

6 Cover the print with greaseproof paper and smooth it with a dry sponge, working from the centre outwards to remove any air bubbles and wrinkles.

7 Remove the greaseproof paper and wipe off any excess paste.

8 Cover the print with another sheet of greaseproof paper and a sheet of card. Weight down until dry.

(Large prints may buckle the backing board as they dry. To prevent this, stick paper roughly the same weight as the print onto the back of the board, using the same technique.)

Hanging pictures
- Use nylon cord or 3-ply picture wire (not string) knotted into D-rings, screw eyes or back hooks.

- Screw eyes are suitable if the moulding of the frame is thick enough to take the screw without splitting.

- For heavy pictures, use back hooks and screw them to the back of the frame mouldings.

- Hang pictures on picture hooks (sold as single or double hooks). These come complete with fine masonry nails that can be hammered into the wall.

- For concrete walls or walls which have been given a concrete coating to prevent damp, use special plastic hooks with three or four short, needle-like nails to hammer in. Beware with these because the nails are intentionally very short, which means they may become dislodged if pulled.

Left *These small plywood corner shelves, placed high up on the wall, provide storage and informal display space.*

This blue glass benefits from the backlighting of a glass-brick window, installed to lighten a basement extension. The arrangement of pictures helps to overcome the rather awkward placing of the long, narrow window.

Living with Children

Designing for young children is difficult because their needs change as they grow older. In a small home the ability to dovetail them into their parents' lives, while providing space for play, requires imaginative use of space. This chest-of-drawers is big enough to house clothes and toys, yet low enough not to overwhelm a small room.

Many families with small children have only one living room, the parents' bedroom and another bedroom for one or more children. In small homes such as this, the planning of the rooms must be very carefully considered so that the space is used in a way tolerable to everyone in the family. It must provide some sort of personal space for each child, even if it is just his or her bed, as well as allowing the children's and the adults' activities to be carried on satisfactorily side by side. Careful assessment of everyone's needs, followed by careful planning of the space and the decoration and furniture, is much more likely to lead to harmonious family life than deciding things piecemeal and hoping for the best.

It is wise to encourage children to take part in choosing the furniture and decor for their own rooms. Even a two-year-old can have strong ideas on what he or she wants and should be allowed a say, no matter what fond parents may have set their hearts on. Children's rooms need, above all, to be practical, versatile and robust. You may long to see a little girl in a garden of flowering prints and ruched curtains but she may prefer primary colours and roller blinds. Nearly all children will prefer space for play to polite furniture.

A small bedroom may be perfectly adequate for sleeping, nappy-changing and dressing because a good deal of play will inevitably take place in the more spacious environment of the living room. The adults will have to accommodate children's paraphernalia amongst their own in the main living space. While children are young, it is sensible to make the most of a simple, friendly and adaptable scheme rather than expect a child to fit into over-planned or sophisticated surroundings. The child should be able to run around with a baby walker without parents fretting about the state of the walls. Sturdy furniture painted bright colours will look better and last longer under childhood conditions. It will also look at home with toys and tiny chairs.

A child's bedroom should be as inviting as possible so that the child is happy to go to bed when the time comes and to play there quietly from time to time. For very

When space is limited, don't try to conceal toys but instead display them in various baskets where they can be easily sorted into categories. The baskets can be grouped together after play and look decorative.

young children, you need a cot or crib of some kind and a chest-of-drawers. The basic furniture should be kept to a minimum so that there is plenty of room to play but, although nappy-changing can be done perfectly well on the floor, a purpose-designed nappy-changing unit is invaluable. A piece of furniture equipped with a changing pad and drawers and shelves for all the bits and pieces such as disposable nappies, powder, cream, bowls of water, towel and so forth takes up very little space.

FLOORING

Smooth, hardwearing, washable and warm are the best qualities for the floor in a child's room. Fitted carpet, although warm and comfortable, is not the most suitable flooring because it is difficult to stand building bricks on and not very easy to wash. If you do want to use carpet, choose one with a non-pile finish so that cars will run, railway track remains coupled and brick edifices won't fall down.

Toy storage is always

problematical. Here designer

Ken Baker has created wooden

runners for standard plastic

boxes, which can easily be

taken out and put back. The

cupboard doors are of birch-

faced blockboard.

When you are laying carpet, it is important that it should have the correct backing. Rubber-backed carpet can be laid directly onto the floor but most other carpets require proper underlay. Newspapers or an old carpet are not satisfactory substitutes and anything woven used as an underlay will cause the carpet to creep.

There are a number of other floor coverings which are smooth and not cold to the touch, and so are very suitable for children's rooms. Cork is warm and comparatively soft, as is linoleum, which is warmer and altogether more sympathetic than vinyl. Both cork and linoleum can be waxed or sealed with a matt seal, and cork is available coated with PVC which makes it very easy to wash.

Matting is another practical and warm option, and the choice of coir, sisal and rush matting is enormous. At one time, the matting had no backing and collected dust underneath but now most have backings which, besides making them easier to clean, also means they are less likely to ruck up. They can even be printed, stencilled or painted to give added colour and interest.

Wood is a good material for children's floors. Elderly floorboards can often be draughty but you can fill the gaps with crumpled newspaper or papier mâché, or lift the boards and relay them closer together. Wood-block and wood-strip floors do not have this problem. An Indian rug decorated with embroidered animals or flowers is one of the cheapest and prettiest ways to add warmth and colour to a child's room. If the floor is so highly polished that it has become slippery, remove all the old polish with white spirit and replace it with a plastic-resin non-slip floor seal.

WALLS AND CEILINGS

It is fun to do your own mural and paint a child's favourite story on the wall. Use a base colour for the background and paint the details on top with emulsion and/or gouache, similar to the technique described on pages 16–17 except that the picture takes the place of the wash coat. An ocean-with-fish theme is easy even for the inexperienced, with the help of illustrations from a book. Children won't expect you to be Michelangelo and will be delighted whatever the result. You can get a landscape onto one small wall or a whole ocean of sea creatures and all the stars in the firmament on the ceiling, given an extra twinkle by the addition of self-stick glowing stars and moons. Friendly pictures of this kind will help children go to sleep at bedtime and will give them something to look at when they are ill.

A section of wall covered in cork tiles provides an exhibition space in which to pin up children's own paintings. Cork tiles covering a whole wall will act as insulation in rooms which suffer from condensation, particularly attics or rooms which open onto a central staircase where draughts make them feel chilly.

Another idea is to have one completely white, washable wall on which children are allowed to draw and scribble. When it is full of artwork, you simply paint over it again. Fixing a blackboard to the wall takes up less space than having a free-standing easel and blackboard. Painting and scribbling activities are very absorbing, keeping children occupied for a long time, and they are good for manual, visual and artistic skills so it is worth providing a permanent place for them.

COTS AND BEDS

It seems extravagant to buy three cots in succession, one for the newborn baby, one for the toddler and yet another when a real bed is needed. It can be very tempting, especially with a first baby, to spend money on pretty ribboned and frilled baby cradles and baskets but such cots last for three months at most and a baby should not sleep in a cot too small for it. A tiny baby can sleep in a cheap cradle or basket; if you have to budget, it is better to spend money on a sturdy cot with bars for the toddler stage, which lasts for about two years. Thereafter

These home-painted murals illustrate a little girl's favourite stories. The cot is sturdy and should last until she is about three. Soft toys sit between the cot and the wall.

a full-size bed or bunk will probably be the last expensive bed you will need to buy.

An answer to the first cot can be to buy a travel cot. There are several good designs available which are flame-retardant, easy to erect and dismantle, but which won't fold up while the baby is asleep. (Some will, so test carefully before you buy.) Many travel cots are simple and attractive, and will last the baby until the age of six months or more. Once outgrown, it will take up little storage space until the next baby comes along. A travel cot is also invaluable on holiday, with the advantage that the baby is already accustomed to it and will not be upset by having to sleep in a strange bed.

When it comes to the second stage, at around six months, and especially in homes where storage space is limited, it may be sensible to buy a cot which can later be converted into a bed. Several shops sell modular systems designed so that items of furniture can be built up next to or on top of one another, to cope with the needs of children as they grow and also to fit the capacity of the room. You don't have to buy the units all at once but can add them on as the child grows older. Such a system might include a low bed (with drawers under-neath to hold toys or clothes), cupboards, chests-of-drawers and shelves. Many modular systems have a choice of painted or natural finishes.

This kind of system is useful when you are trying to fit furniture round existing radiators and doors. For exam-ple, you could place a narrow chest-of-drawers on either side of a radiator, with a wide shelf/worktop placed over it. This would provide plenty of storage and workspace, and would also direct the heat from the radiator into the room, keeping the child warm when he or she was seated at the desk (always a chilly occupation). As well as the conventional cupboard, shelf and drawer units, many modules include double-height and double-width units, desk units and accessories such as hanging racks, hooks and mirrors. It should be possible to work out an ideal combination for any particular situation.

Modular systems are normally bought as kits to assemble at home and should come complete with screws, handles and instructions. Whether you buy them in a shop or receive them by mail order, the first thing to do is check that all the pieces specified are actually there, as well as the instructions.

When they were first introduced, bunk beds were the ideal way to allow each child their own bed in a small home. Nowadays bunks can also be a way of using space efficiently by giving a child more room for playing, homework, clothes, etc. In their most basic form, bunks can be a couple of solid chests-of-drawers with a bed base laid across them and a mattress, plus, of course, a guard rail and a simple ladder, but there are now many variations on this simple idea. Some supply room underneath the bunk to use as play space, storage space for toys or hanging space for clothes. Make sure that all bunks have safety rails and that they are solid and secure. Some double bunks are designed with the option of being used as twin beds.

If space is desperately cramped, folding foam beds can be used for older children but they are never satisfactory for long-term use. It requires effort and discipline to unfold and make up a bed every time it is needed, something which is fine on holiday or short visits but becomes very tiresome as a daily routine. When buying any foam furniture, make sure it conforms to safety regulations and is covered in fire-retardant fabric. Foam is highly poisonous if it catches fire.

WORK AND PLAY

There should be plenty of room for books and writing things, as well as a well-lit place to write comfortably. There should also be adequate background lighting in the room, and reading lights by the bed and over the desk area.

If toys are played with in the living room, try, if you can, to put up with them for the whole day and then sort and store them in the evening, otherwise you will be putting

game or activity laid out, say a zoo or racing track. If this is fixed to a pulley mechanism, it can be lowered at certain times for play. It will need to have supports to stop it swinging about and you should make sure the pulley rope is strong enough to carry the weight of the board, that it is out of the reach of young children and that it is always in good condition and unfrayed.

A SHARED BEDROOM

If you have to share a bedroom with your new baby, the most pressing need is to provide a degree of privacy for the parents. Again, planning the space is important. There are advantages to sharing: you know at once if the child is restless at night and can comfort it and get it back to sleep almost before it (or you) has woken up. Nursing mothers may also find sharing the room convenient for night feeds.

A very young baby does not take up much room. A small crib and a storage unit are the only essentials, although a comfortable low chair for feeding is a good idea. A folding screen will help to provide a certain amount of privacy and can be fitted with rails or hooks for hanging tiny clothes, so that it becomes dual-purpose.

Alternatively the cot area can be screened by a row of chests or shelving units, either tall or low, which will also act as storage. Nappy-changing can take place on the parental bed, with its essential equipment stored in a bedside table. Play equipment can be stored in the living room if necessary, or spread around there and the bathroom and perhaps the hall.

UNUSUAL PLAY AREAS

Places which seem claustrophobic or simply too small for sensible adult use often have a particular attraction for children. For small children who need constant supervision, there is that good old place under the stairs.

For a teenager's room, watery blue emulsion was brushed over the white base coat and some of the blue paint was then rubbed off with rags.

be trusted on their own. They need to be able to cope with ladder-like stairs and must know they should not light matches.

The sloping roof of an attic can provide an intimate world-of-their-own feeling in which to run a permanent train track or provide private space for reading, music or socializing. Attics are often chilly in winter and suffocating in summer, particularly if the roof space is uninsulated. Insulation is usually inexpensive however, and you may be eligible for a grant. A cheap and fairly effective way to insulate is to fix coarse insulation cork tiles to the sloping walls and ceiling. The strong smell of cork soon fades and if you wish you can seal the tiles or paint them. The tiles make good noticeboards.

If you want to use an attic as a bedroom, all the furniture should be low so that taller children will not knock their heads. Beds can be of the futon type or simply mattresses on the floor. If it is to be a workspace, place the desk under a window to get the full light and sit on the room side where the slope of the roof is not at its lowest. A good place for a workspace is in the alcove made by a mansard roof, which will be slightly higher than the rest of the room. Always make sure there is some means of escape in case of fire. For heating, place a radiator on a wall where there is no window. Use very low chests for storage and have plenty of hooks for hanging things from.

Children love small furniture their own size, so if you set up a child-sized table and chairs they will be drawn to them like magnets. Under the stairs is separate but near enough to adults to feel safe; the space is their own and it feels private. Staircases which are part of the living room provide space which can be completely supervised and this is obviously the best for very young children. Older children who can be allowed a certain amount of unsupervised play will prefer to be under the hall stairs, particularly if it is warm and well lit.

Other areas which attract children are attics and basements, but these are only for older children who can

Basements are invaluable for older children who want independence and to make a noise, or at least a different sort of noise to their parents. Basements are, however, likely to suffer from damp and darkness. The damp is most likely to be caused by a faulty damp-proof course or, in older houses, no damp-proof course at all. Get the damp dealt with professionally before you try to use the basement. If you wish, you can also treat the walls inside with one of the various water-repellent treatments available. Cover the floor with warm rugs or matting, and it will be an excellent place for a rocking horse, music system, TV, video, computer and other time- and space-consuming items loved by children.

SAFETY

People feel very secure in their own homes and are usually unaware of what a very dangerous place the home really is, especially for small children who are inexperienced, unsteady on their feet and insatiably curious. These are some of the dangers to plan against.

Stairs

- Stairs should be well lit so that shadows do not confuse.

- Staircarpet should be well fitted and taut, with no loose stair rods or rucked-up areas which could cause a child to trip.

- If young children live in the house, there should be a child safety gate at the bottom and top of the stairs until they learn to negotiate them safely by themselves. This is particularly important in houses which have steep, narrow staircases and it is worth teaching an active toddler how to come downstairs backwards. Until you have achieved that, it is essential to have a gate.

Floors

- All floors should be non-slip.

- Carpets should be smooth and flat and not rucked up.

- Vinyl, cork and linoleum tiles should be undamaged and properly stuck down, particularly at the corners.

- Carpets on stairs and floors should be in good repair.

Electricity

- Electric power points should be fitted flush to the wall and out of reach of young children.

- Electric leads should not trail over the floor.

- Lights in children's rooms should be fixed to the wall or ceiling so that they cannot be knocked over.

- Electric sockets should be covered with socket guards.

- Buy electrical equipment with an official safety-approved label on it, which shows that it has been checked and has passed certain safety regulations. If using foreign equipment, check that it is suitable for use with the voltage of the country you are living in.

Doors and windows

- Doors leading outside, or to a hall or landing, should be protected with safety locks and handles which young children cannot operate on their own.

This secondhand bed was found in France. There is space underneath for storing toys, and the bed is big enough to last until the child reaches adulthood.

- Fix protective metal bars or a grid to the frames of upstairs windows, at least on the lower half of the window.

Bathroom
- Shower doors should be made of plastic or glass covered in safety film so that it will not splinter if it breaks.

- Make sure the flooring is non-slip, and use non-slip bathmats.

- Bathroom heaters should be wall-mounted and children should not be able to reach the switches from the bath.

- Use a rubber safety mat in the bath.

- Fit doors with two-way bolt indicators which can be opened from the outside.

- Install a high door handle to stop a child entering the bathroom alone.

- Fix the medicine cabinet out of child's reach and keep it locked. All medicines must be stored here. Eighteen-month to two-and-a-half-year-olds are the main victims of home-poisoning accidents and aspirin is the main cause.

Kitchen
- Fit safety catches on cupboards and drawers to prevent children from getting into them.

- Keep high chairs away from worktops, doors and through areas so that children cannot reach anything dangerous, and also so that you will not trip over the legs. Children should always wear a safety harness in the kitchen.

- In a small kitchen it is particularly important to prevent children bumping into things, knocking over pans or playing with the cooker.

- Install cooker guards to keep prying fingers away.

- It is better to have rounded edges on tables than square ones as children are less likely to knock into them when they are running around.

- Make sure you have a non-slip floor and wipe up all grease spills immediately.

- Divide the kitchen, if it is big enough, with a waist-high storage unit and a gate so that children can play within sight but out of danger.

- The most convenient place for cleaning equipment is unfortunately under the sink, which is also the most dangerous. Keep chemical cleaners and all poisonous substances in a locked cupboard well out of reach of a two-year-old standing on a chair.

- The following are all poisonous: adhesives, air-freshener blocks, ammonia, bleach, upholstery and carpet cleaners, dyes, detergents, disinfectants, dry-cleaning fluids, paint solvents, fertilizer liquids, marking ink, insecticides, matchheads, metal polish, moth treatments, oven cleaners, paint strippers, shoe polish, paraffin, scouring powders, silver polish, lavatory cleaners, turpentine, washing powders, washing-up liquids and window-cleaning preparations.

Fires
- Never leave any fire unguarded. The best guards are made of metal mesh and are about 90cm (3ft) high and 1.2m (4ft) wide, with sides which prevent a child from getting anywhere near the fire.

- Place a piece of furniture in front of hot radiators or hot pipes to prevent young children bumping into them by accident.

- Do not use a portable paraffin heater in a room where a child may be left alone.

Creative Ideas for Fabrics

Fabrics provide important contrasts of texture. The charm of handwoven fabrics against hard, shiny surfaces can effectively take the mind of the size of a space, as you can see from this small room. The traditional woven kilim is hung from a wooden beam, and the small blue sofa, covered with another kilim, looks really sumptuous against the terracotta tiles.

Textiles offer some of the most versatile ways of giving colour, warmth, softness and mystery to an interior. The choice of fabrics and textiles available today is staggering. There is practically nothing you cannot buy for your home, from innumerable prints to the practical, washable simplicity of cotton gingham and muslin, or richly woven traditional paisley designs and kilim rugs. Fabric can be used to soften hard lines, conceal ugly shapes, cover up worn upholstery and to add a touch of luxury or a splash of colour. Cast your eyes round your home and you will see a dozen ways in which you could use fabric to give a new, fresh touch.

In small rooms, plain fabrics or overall patterns usually look better than enormous grandiose prints. Both prints and weaves can be successfully mixed and matched with other patterns and colours, provided there is some unifying factor such as the basic colour or the type of pattern.

CURTAINS AND BLINDS

Short curtains can look good in tiny cottage windows or in attics with sloping roofs, but in general curtains look more graceful and generous when full length and, in many cases, when drawn right across one wall. If this would cover a radiator or take up too much wall space, it might be worth thinking about blinds instead of curtains. Full-length curtains should just touch the floor. Theoretically, the fabric can trail on the floor but in a small space this is inviting people to tread on or trip over it and it looks as though the curtains are too long by accident rather than design. However, you do need to make sure there are generous hems to allow for shrinkage when the curtains are washed.

It is normally considered best for curtains to be lined. This certainly helps them to hang well and provides better insulation than when they are unlined. However, if there is not much wall space to draw the curtains back to, it may be better to use a sheer material such as dralon which will hang well on its own but not be bulky. Very sheer curtains (say, muslin) can be hung, knotted and draped effectively. Other suitable fabrics are mattress ticking and glazed chintz, which has a built-in stiffness that helps it to hang well. Gingham and other starched and sprightly cottons will also hang unlined, specially at small windows. As part of a formal scheme, however, curtains should always be lined and even interlined; interlining provides excellent insulation in front of draughty windows.

If you want to hang curtains from rods or a curtain track, make sure the rod or track is wider than the windows so that the curtains can be pulled well back. This gives a much better effect and makes the windows look larger. Otherwise you can keep them permanently closed at the top and looped back at the sides with tie bands during the day.

Lace makes pretty curtains and white cotton lace can be bought in charming pictorial designs and in different depths of the same design. Lace is not just a substitute for net curtains, but decoration in its own right.

Roller blinds may be a better choice than curtains, especially if you want to use a windowsill for storage or display. Blinds can be made of any thin, closely woven fabric and you can even make them yourself from a kit and the fabric of your choice. The kit includes the roller, small tacks and stiffening spray. Matchstick or pinoleum blinds (blinds with narrow slats) take up no more space than roller blinds. Install a blind if a window is set tight into a corner, unless you decide to run glass shelves across the window and use it for displays of glass or growing plants.

It is difficult to know how to screen windows set into a sloping roof. The fabric needs to be anchored at the bottom as well as the top so that it does not hang away from the window. You can string sheer fabric onto stretch wires (of the kind normally used for net curtains), fixed to the top and bottom frame. Alternatively, fit a roller blind with rings at the bottom to slot over hooks in the wall or in the bottom windowframe.

WALLS AND CEILINGS

All sorts of textiles can be hung on walls—tapestries, tweed, suede, hessian, silk, flannel and, of course, kilim rugs. Fabric panels can be used to cover one wall or to line a whole room, acting as a kind of insulating wallpaper. Single pieces of fabric look effective hung individually as a feature.

You can use a staple gun to attach fabric directly on the wall but a better method is to fix the fabric to battens (see page 93). It is hardly worth buying a staple gun for this but they can sometimes be hired from tool hire stores. If the fabric is plain, pictures and prints can be hung on top so you will not have wasted any display space.

Individual hand-woven tapestries can be hung from rods or poles fixed to a picture rail. Kilims make excellent hangings, being weighty and in colours which co-ordinate with many interior styles. If you have a lighter-weight hanging, such as a batik, you could weight the bottom by sewing small ballbearings in the hem so that it hangs well.

Ceilings can be softened, and ugly ceilings concealed, with looped fabric. This is specially suitable for halls where a very little fabric can conceal a multitude of gas and electric meters and other unfortunate sights. Muslin is cheap and effective because it drapes prettily and is unobtrusive. All you have to do is make a hem at each end wide enough to get a rod (a bamboo or a narrow wooden batten) through and fix the rods to the ceiling. You could perhaps create another channel halfway along the length of fabric for an extra rod, allowing plenty of fabric to loop between them.

Narrow rooms can be treated in the same way, with the fabric caught at intervals to create a scalloped effect. This is very good for concealing unsightly ceiling treatments and for lowering the ceiling to make the space less box-like. It does not matter if the fabric is not quite as wide as the ceiling—a few centimetres each side will not be noticeable.

The most basic screen looks exotic when covered in well-chosen fabric. It will hide a multitude of sins or screen a sleeping baby. This one is draped in lace, but the fabric can be changed at will.

FABRICS ON FURNITURE

Fitted upholstery covers are expensive, but fabric can be used more cheaply—and with much greater potential for change—to make temporary covers for upholstery which you are tired of or which is becoming worn. The advantage of temporary covers is that you can whip them off and substitute something else at a moment's notice while you have the previous covers drycleaned or washed, then fold and store them in the airing cupboard until you next feel like a change.

Any sort of fabric can be thrown over an armchair or

cover made out of a kilim should last virtually for ever. The most suitable furniture shapes for ethnic weaving are simple, old-fashioned sofas and armchairs, ottomans and upholstered stools.

A simple but substantial white or oatmeal-coloured fabric such as tweed or a slubbed cotton can give a 'busy' room a surprising elegance, both separating and combining the various elements and giving a sense of order. A piece of upholstered seating can be given a new look by making loose covers for the cushions and arms, and simply laying a length of the same fabric across the whole piece. White or off-white net, cotton or muslin curtains would continue the theme and help to calm an over-filled room.

Another useful piece of furniture is a screen. Folding screens were used in the past to create pockets of warmth in draughty homes, where open fireplaces caused cold winds to rush in through the door and up the chimney. They have been rather out of fashion since central heating came in but they can be invaluable for psychologically dividing one part of a room from another. Depending on how they are covered, they make an attractive addition to a room, with the advantage that they can be moved around, placed in different positions and even put away when not needed.

Screens do not have to be elaborately fitted, with the fabric measured, turned in and tacked. You can throw fabric casually over them and change it whenever you wish. Antique lace is perfect for a feminine bedroom and a heavy-textured weave will look good in a living/workroom.

If you are using a small table for displaying small objects, a tablecloth always looks elegant, particularly if the table itself is not very attractive. A cloth which falls to the floor will conceal a table made of an old cable spool laid on top of an upturned box and nobody will be any the wiser. Again, a fabric which drapes softly makes the best tablecloth. You can cover the cloth with lace or another small cloth in a contrasting colour.

Experiment with various colours and patterns. The

A new armchair has been given character by imaginative use of different fabrics, including two tweeds and various cushion covers.

sofa, but a soft fabric with some 'give' will mould itself to the form of the chair in a particularly satisfactory way. The textiles which ideally lend themselves to large pieces of furniture are jacquard-woven 'throws' in paisley or all-over floral designs, often taken from millefleurs tapestries. They may be all-wool, or wool and acrylic, to give the necessary suppleness and softness to drape over the contours of a sofa. Woven woollen rugs, tweed or tartan travel rugs, rag rugs and Indian prints (Indian bedspreads are good for this) will all brighten up elderly furniture.

Kilims can be used to throw over furniture, and a fitted

pattern should not be so strong that it conflicts with the things you want to display. If the objects are small, it would probably be best to use a plain fabric or at least a very discreet pattern.

BEDROOMS

One of the cheapest ways to 'redecorate' a bedroom is to change the pillowcases or bedcover, which can revive a room quite surprisingly. The choice of bedcovers and pillowcases in bedding departments often makes one forget the opportunities for making them at home. Some pillowcases are made with a different pattern on each side so you can ring the changes by mixing and matching them. This is another idea that would be easy and cheap to do yourself.

Two Indian bedspreads can become an unusual duvet cover and there are many other interesting fabrics to use, perhaps to get away from the idea that bedrooms should be flowery and feminine. The important thing is to choose a cotton which is fine and soft; you don't want anything scratchy in bed.

Quilted comforters, which are not as bulky as duvets or eiderdowns, add extra warmth in winter without adding much weight. They fold away into next to nothing for storage and, if the fabric is chosen carefully, will provide a different winter colour for the room.

Traditional patchwork quilts were made of old pieces of fabric and clothes so that nothing was ever wasted. Modern quilts may be in traditional designs or very carefully chosen fabrics in modern designs. They are often works of art which are better hung on the wall than spread over a bed (see page 93 for instructions on hanging fabric from battens).

A canopy over the bed can be in almost any fabric because it will not suffer from wear and tear. Lace, voile, muslin, sprigged cotton or Indonesian batik will create a summery effect and brocade, velvet or woven fabrics will make you feel warm in winter.

CUSHIONS

Cushions are another quick and simple way to bring a jaded interior to life or to introduce a touch of the exotic. They can also transform a newly designed interior which seems a little too tasteful or bland.

In many homes cushions become a feature in their own right, providing comfortable support on shabby chairs and sofas or used as floor seating, specially for children. It is usually best to buy the cushions from a cheap supplier and to buy the fabric or made-up covers separately; buying cushions and covers together is an expensive way of doing things.

If you are grouping cushions, choose colours and fabrics which either match each other or complement the existing furnishings in the room. If it is a fairly formal room and you have chosen pale colours and sophisticated curtain treatments, such as ruched curtains with large pelmets, then the cushions should be carefully made with frills and piping in toning colours. Pale golds and greens would not be flattered by scarlet but would be better with deep greens and golds. A room with an ethnic look, with kilims on the floor and curtains in Indian-printed cotton, would look better with a group of cushions in ethnic embroideries and deep-coloured prints, with no need for frills or piping. Very feminine rooms look pretty with smaller cushions than normal in lace or broderie anglaise covers, perhaps even with small bows.

Floor cushions were at one time very fashionable but if you are not actually using them they are liable to get in the way and are difficult to store. Instead, two pillows can be fitted into one large square cushion cover so that you have pillows for the spare bed or sofa-bed when visitors stay, but can conceal the spare bed with big and small cushions as a divan when they leave.

If you buy or make cushion covers the same shape as pillowcases, you can use pillows inside them so that when you have guests all you have to do is substitute pillowcases for the cushion covers.

A large modern chair has been covered in black-and-white fabric and cushions to provide seating, a place to fling coats and bags, and style.

Fabrics which drape well can be slightly gathered as though they were curtains, implying there might be a window behind them. This is a good trick for covering a bad piece of plastering or some other eyesore you are stuck with.

CO-ORDINATING AND MATCHING

Interesting effects can be obtained by mixing different patterns and colours. Equally, a very small, 'bitty' room can be held together with matching fabric throughout. Unless you choose harsh colours or large patterns, such use of fabric is seldom overpowering but it does pull a scheme together, particularly in a small space.

THE UNEXPECTED

Textiles are perfect for concealing horrible sights as well as for framing a pretty view. Drape a large woven camel-bag over the arm of a chair to hold magazines, or use a larger one to store firewood or bedlinen. For a really unusual idea, an Indian fabric 'arch' makes a welcoming entrance to a home, transforming the ordinary into something stylish.

If you have a platform bed in a room which already has rather a low ceiling, the ceiling may seem to bear down on the occupant in an unpleasant claustrophobic way. It can be concealed by creating a sort of tent, which feels cosy and enclosed rather than threatening. The most elaborate method is to attach the fabric at a central point on the ceiling and to allow it to fall away to a point on the walls where it is caught and secured, then allowed to fall to the ground or to mattress level. Alternatively, you can run a curtain rod along the side of the bed, which will screen it from the rest of the room.

Places which seem irredeemably cramped and bleak can be miraculously cheered by the tiniest amount of fabric. A remnant of cotton print can even make a

BLURRING THE EDGES

One of the ways to make a space feel larger is to conceal its boundaries; if the edges are blurred and the corners mysterious, the space is undefined and automatically seems larger.

You can drape fabric from the centre of the ceiling. This will work in a room where there is minimal 'stuff' but not in a home where there are children or activities which need elbow room. However, draping the fabric in shallow loops across the ceiling only takes up ceiling space and leaves more room for living.

gathered skirt round a lavatory cistern, using humour and invention to transform the room.

A SIMPLE WAY
TO COVER AN ARMCHAIR OR SOFA

Calculate the length of the fabric you need by measuring up from the floor, up and over the seat, over the back and down to the floor again, allowing an extra 30cm (12in) for tucking in and hems. Gather the excess fabric round the arm and tie with cord. Tuck the fabric well into the back of the chair. Alternatively lay a piece of fabric over the basic furniture shape and make separate cushion covers and arm covers.

HOW TO HANG FABRICS

Large, heavy hangings such as rugs, tapestries and patchwork quilts, can be displayed in several ways. If you are hanging anything you think might be valuable or which you particularly like, remember that any strong light will cause it to fade so don't shine spotlamps on it or place it where it is in direct sunlight.

Woven tapestries should be lined before they are hung. Send large pieces to an expert; your local antique shop should be able to advise. If you decide to do it yourself, use pre-shrunk linen or brown holland and cut it to length, allowing 5cm (2in) all round for turnings. Lay the tapestry face down on a flat surface, place the lining on top and pin the centre vertical. Use button thread to stitch parallel lines about 30cm (12in) apart. Then stitch horizontal rows across the tapestry and lining, catching a warp thread of the tapestry. Let it hang for a few weeks before hemstitching the bottom.

Hanging with Velcro
Stitch Velcro to the back of the lining, through to the hanging, along all sides. Nail the rough half of the Velcro

to battens and fix them to the wall. To hang, press the Velcro on the fabric onto the Velcro on the wall.

Hanging with loops
Sew tabs to the back of the hanging to make loops. Thread a rod or bamboo cane through the loops and hang from hooks in the wall.

Fixing fabric to battens
You can staple fabric directly onto the wall, either turning in the raw edges or covering them with braid, but you will get a more professional result if you use battens.

This small home has been given an exotic and welcoming entrance with an embroidered canopy.

This tiny entrance hall houses electricity and gas meters, and bare light bulbs in the ceiling. Looping muslin over the whole area conceals the ugly mess and gives a pleasant diffused light; it can easily be unhooked for access.

1 Fix thin strips of wood along the top and bottom of the wall, just below the ceiling moulding and just above the wainscot.

2 Nail vertical strips of wood at 2m (6ft) intervals.

3 Attach the first fabric panel by centring it between the outside edge of the first vertical strip and the middle of the second, keeping the top of the fabric level with the top of the horizontal batten. Lightly tack it in the middle. Stretch the fabric to each side, tack it and then staple it in position.

4 Attach the rest of the panels in the same way, working from centre to centre of the upright battens until the last one, then fix the edge of the fabric to the outside edge of that.

If the fabric is thin, staple lining fabric to the battens first. Choose fabric that is the same colour as the main fabric or marginally paler.

Index